A POCKET GUIDE TO
INSECTS

Patrick Hook

Bath · New York · Singapore · Hong Kong · Cologne · Delhi · Melbourne

This edition published by Parragon
in 2009

Parragon
Chartist House
15-17 Trim Street
Bath, BA1 1HA, UK
www.parragon.com

Produced by Focus Publishing
Designer Heather McMillan
Project Editor Guy Croton
Indexer Caroline Watson

See page 256 for photograph
copyright details
Text © Parragon Books Ltd 2008

ISBN 978-1-4075-8746-2
Printed in China

CONTENTS

INTRODUCTION 10–19

Insect Structure and Form 12   Insect Nervous Systems   15

Insect Anatomy Scheme   14   Insect Sizes   18

THE LIFE OF AN INSECT 20–41

Insect Life-Cycles   22   Habitats   37

Evolution   30   Human-Insect Interaction   38

Communication   31   Insect Predators   39

Locomotion   34   Conservation   39

Behavior and Sociality   36   Naming and Taxonomy   41

BUTTERFLIES 42–79

Monarch	44	Painted Lady	65
Large Skipper	46	Black Swallowtail	66
Millet Skipper	47	Orange Tip	68
Brown Argus	48	Clouded Yellow	69
Green Hairstreak	49	Brimstone	70
Holly Blue	50	Large White	71
Small Copper	51	Small White	72
Common Blue	52	Bath White	73
Brown Hairstreak	54	Ringlet	74
Small Tortoiseshell	56	Small Heath	75
Dark Green Fritillary	58	Grayling	76
Silver-Washed Fritillary	60	Meadow Brown	77
Marsh Fritillary	61	Speckled Wood	78
Peacock	62	Gatekeeper	79
Comma	64		

MOTHS 80–101

White Ermine	82
Cinnabar Moth	83
Peppered Moth	84
Gray Dagger	85
Angle Shades	86
Green Silver-lines	87
Iron Prominent	88
Lobster Moth	89
Emperor Moth	90
Death's-Head Hawkmoth	92
Elephant Hawkmoth	93
Small Elephant Hawkmoth	94
Hummingbird Hawkmoth	96
Lime Hawkmoth	98
Privet Hawkmoth	99
Six-Spot Burnet	100

DRAGONFLIES & DAMSELFLIES
102–129

Dragonflies	104	Damselflies	116
Southern Hawker	105	Banded Demoiselle	117
Halloween Pennant	106	Beautiful Demoiselle	118
Broad-Bodied Chaser	108	Azure Damselfly	120
Eight-Spotted Skimmer	110	Common Blue Damselfly	122
Widow Skimmer	111	Large Red Damselfly	123
Twelve-Spotted Skimmer	112	Mayflies	124
Epaulet Skimmer	113	Stoneflies	126
Common Darter	114	Caddisflies	128
Violet Darter/Dropwing	115		

FLIES   130–145

Yellow Dung Fly	132	Hoverflies	138
Black Scavenger Fly	134	Horse Flies	140
European Crane Fly	135	Mosquitoes	142
Robber Flies	136	Blow-flies	144

BEES, WASPS, SAWFLIES, & ANTS 146–167

Bees	148	Sawflies	160
Honey Bees	150	Green Sawfly	161
Bumblebees	152	Hornets	162
Wasps	154	Oriental Hornet	163
Red-Brown Paper Wasp	156	Ants	164
Giant Ichneumon Wasp	157	Southern Wood Ant	166
Sphecid Wasps	158	Black Ant	167

GRASSHOPPERS, CRICKETS, & LOCUSTS 168–181

Grasshoppers	170	Great Green Bush Cricket	177
Meadow Grasshopper	171	Mole Crickets	178
Blue-Winged Grasshopper	172	True Crickets	180
Common Green Grasshopper	173		
Bush Crickets	174		
Speckled Bush Cricket	175		
Dark Bush Cricket	176		

TRUE BUGS 182–205

Froghoppers	184	Water Scorpion	195
Black & Red Froghopper	185	Water Boatman	196
Shield Bugs	186	Water Cricket	197
Dock Leaf Bug	188	Cicadas	198
Red-Black Shield Bug	190	Periodical Cicadas	199
Green Shield Bug	191	Aphids	200
Water Bugs	192	Rose Aphid	201
Common Pond Skater	193	Mealybugs	202
Water Measurer	194	Scale Insects	204

BEETLES 206–227

Soldier Beetle	208	Ladybugs	222
Black-Tipped Soldier Beetle	209	2-Spot Ladybug	224
Golden Ground beetle	210	7-Spot Ladybug	225
Klamath Weed Beetle	211	14-Spot Ladybug	226
Poplar Leaf Beetle	212		
Green Dock Leaf Beetle	214		
Black Vine Weevil	215		
Green Leaf Weevil	216		
Thick-Legged Flower Beetle	217		
Common Cockchafer	218		
Wasp Beetle	220		
Two-Banded Longhorn	221		

NEUROPTERANS 228–235

Lacewings	230	Ant Lion	233
Giant or Stream Lacewing	231	Common Alder Fly	234
Antlions	232	European Owlfly	235

OTHER INSECT ORDERS 236–249

European Earwig	238	Common Scorpionfly	243
Western Drywood Termite	239	Stick Insects	244
Hog Louse	240	Leaf Insects	246
Empusid Mantis	241	Silverfish	248
European Praying Mantis	242		

Glossary	250
Index	252
Picture Credits	256

INTRODUCTION

Insects, which are classified in the Class Insecta, are found in almost every kind of habitat on Earth, in a spectacular array of forms. They are the most numerous and diverse group of all animals, and the vast majority have never been formally identified. There are currently over a million described species, yet some experts think that there may be as many as ten million in total. So far, science has recorded around 360,000 species of beetle, 180,000 species of butterfly and moth, 120,000 fly species, 110,000 species of bees, wasps, and ants, 82,000 true bug species, 20,000 species of grasshoppers, 5,000 dragonfly species, 2,000 praying mantids, and many, many others. Tragically, large numbers of insects across the world are being made extinct as the result of human activities such as rampant deforestation and widespread pollution.

Opposite: Ladybugs are members of the beetle family.

Insect Structure and Form

Insects—along with arachnids, crustaceans, and others—are arthropods. These are creatures with segmented bodies covered with an exoskeleton made of chitin. This is divided into a head, thorax, and abdomen. They typically have appendages on each segment; on the head these are in the form of antennae and external mouthparts. The thorax has six legs attached to it, and in the winged species, two pairs of wings (one pair is often vestigial). It also houses any associated wing muscles. The abdomen carries all the organs required for respiration, reproduction, and digestion.

Adult insects have three pairs of legs.

Ticks have eight legs, and are therefore not actually insects...

Insect larvae may seem to have lots of legs, but in fact they actually only have three pairs that function as limbs. The others are known as "false," or "pseudo" legs.

An insect's exoskeleton has to perform a variety of functions. One of the most important of these is to provide a rigid structure so that the flight and leg muscles and attachment points of the insect can work efficiently. The exoskeleton also provides a degree of protection against predators—although the extent to which this is necessary varies tremendously from one insect to another. Some insects, for example, are highly toxic, and so do not need hard armor to protect themselves. Others, such as aphids, simply form close alliances with ants and gain protection from them, rather than protecting themselves. The exoskeleton itself is made up of two layers: the outer one is called the epicuticle—this is thin, has a waxy coating, and is primarily used to prevent water loss or ingress. The layer below it is called the procuticle, a structure primarily composed of chitin, which is a very tough, but flexible material.

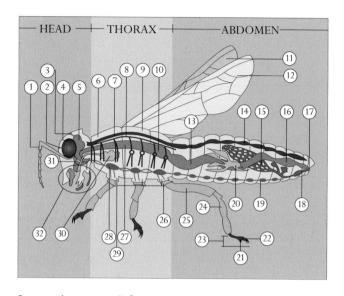

Insect Anatomy Scheme

1 antenna
2 ocelli (lower)
3 ocelli (upper)
4 compound eye
5 brain (cerebral ganglia)
6 prothorax
7 dorsal artery
8 tracheal tubes
  (trunk with spiracle)
9 mesothorax
10 metathorax
11 first wing
12 second wing
13 mid-gut (stomach)
14 heart
15 ovary
16 hind-gut
  (intestine, rectum, and anus)

17 anus
18 vagina
19 nerve chord
  (abdominal ganglia)
20 Malpighian tubes
21 pillow
22 claws
23 tarsus
24 tibia
25 femur
26 trochanter
27 fore-gut (crop, gizzard)
28 thoracic ganglion
29 coxa
30 salivary gland
31 sub-oesophageal ganglion
32 mouthparts

Insect Nervous Systems

The nervous systems of insects are relatively simple, and yet function extremely well. They are composed of a brain and a ventral nerve cord. This is a pathway made up from a network of ganglia that are made up from neurons linked together by synapses. The nervous system is distributed throughout the body, making it much less centralized than that of higher animals.

Insects have three different kinds of sensing receptors—these are photoreceptors, which detect the amount of and quality of light (including color), chemoreceptors, which detect smell or taste, and mechanoreceptors, which determine the presence of mechanical vibrations or movements. These are used in sense organs that allow insects to see, smell, taste, hear, and touch what is around them.

Not all insects have the full complement of senses—some, such as termite workers and various cave-dwelling species—are often blind. Apart from these exceptions, most insects have a pair of compound eyes. Each of these is constructed of many (up to several thousand) photoreceptor cells called "ommatidia." Many species, such as dragonflies, hunt by sight, and so have evolved superb vision. What they see, however, is not the same as humans might see. Many are sensitive to different parts of the light spectrum. Some, such as butterflies, can see well into the

Dragonflies and damselflies hunt using their superb eyesight.

ultra-violet, for example—this allows them to see nectar-producing flowering plants more easily. They, along with honeybees and bumblebees, are able to perceive true colors, whereas many other insects have much more limited color perception abilities.

Some of the ways that insects sense their environments are somewhat unusual; butterflies, for instance, can taste with their feet. One of the most interesting examples of insect senses, however, is found in certain night-flying moths, especially some of those in the Geometridae family. These small to medium-sized creatures are able to detect the ultra-sonic radiation used by bats to hunt their prey. Many have an automatic response mechanism which activates whenever a bat flies nearby; the insect's wings close, causing them to fall immediately to the ground, away from the bat predator and out of harm's way. In a fascinating extension of this, a few species have evolved a method of actively generating a counter-signal to "jam" the bat's ultra-sonic detection system.

Below: Small Tortoiseshell.   *Opposite: Sycamore Moth caterpillar.*

Insect Sizes

The maximum size of insects is limited by the way that they breathe. This is done via a series of internal pipes called tracheal tubes. These are linked to the atmosphere by small openings called spiracles, and oxygen reaches the body tissues mostly as the result of diffusion and a certain amount of muscular pumping. The spiracles can be opened or closed at will, allowing insects to regulate the amount of moisture that they lose to the air and preventing the ingress of water. This is especially important in those insects which live underwater or in very damp places.

There is quite a lot of debate as to which are the heaviest living insects in the world, but some say they are the Giant Wetas, a kind of giant grasshopper from New Zealand. These creatures can reach more than 2.5 oz (70 g), which is more than the weight of an adult sparrow. There are also several species of large beetles that would certainly be in contention for the title of heaviest insect. These include the Goliath beetles (Scarabaeidae) and Longhorn beetles (Cerambycidae), which are found in the rainforests of Africa and South America.

The Longhorn Beetle.

The Atlas Moth, one of the largest flying insects in the world.

The longest insects are stick insects in the order Phasmatodea, with females of the species *Phobaeticus serratipes* reaching around 22 in (555 mm) in the resting position. At the other end of the scale, some fully-grown insects are tiny. The smallest are those in a group known as Fairyflies—these are parasitic wasps in the family Mymaridae. The blind and wingless males of the species *Dicopomorpha echmepterygis* from the United States are considered to be the smallest, and grow to a maximum length of only 0.005 in (0.139 mm).

The largest flying insects in the world include the Atlas moth, *Attacus atlas*, which is a member of the Saturniidae family. It has the greatest wing area, and is found in south-east Asia. The females of this species can have a wingspan of up to 10–12 in (25–30 cm) across. The largest overall wingspan, however, is that of the White Witch or Great Owlet moth (*Thysania agrippina*)—it is a member of the Noctuidae family, and it can measure 12 in (31 cm) from wingtip to wingtip.

THE LIFE OF
AN INSECT

INSECT LIFE-CYCLES

Unlike many other animals, insects have to go through a complicated series of stages to reach adulthood. This process—known as metamorphosis—characteristically begins with an egg that hatches into a larva. It then undergoes several stages called "instars," each of which is separated by a skin molt. At the final molt, the larva changes into a pupa, and then emerges from this some time later as an adult. However, this is an oversimplification of the process, as there are three entirely different types of metamorphic cycle. These are known as ametabolous, hemimetabolous, and holometabolous processes.

Ametabolous insects, such as bristletails, emerge from the egg as small versions of the adult and simply grow bigger until they themselves are adult-sized and sexually mature. Hemimetabolous insects emerge from the egg as nymphs (terrestrial species) or naiads (aquatic species), and change into adults via a series of small changes at each molt. Holometabolous insects undergo the full process outlined above—namely an egg, followed by the larva, then a pupa, and finally the adult. The timing of the changes in all three metamorphic regimes may be linked to a number of environmental conditions, but are ultimately controlled by the release of special hormones by the brain.

Opposite: Butterfly pupae waiting for emergence.

Praying Mantis eggs are laid in a single mass known as an "ootheca."

Eggs

Although most insects lay eggs—a process called "ovipary"—in some species the eggs actually hatch inside the female's body and are delivered as live young; this is known as "vivipary." There are many different ways in which insect eggs are laid. Some are deposited singly or in groups in precise locations, whereas others are simply scattered over suitable ground. Some parasitic wasps lay their eggs directly into those of their host species using a special egg-laying tube called an ovipositor. Others may be laid in all manner of places, depending on the species concerned. These include on dead or dying animals, into piles of dung, on plants, in the soil, into the living body tissues of other insects, into tree trunks, or almost any other location where sustenance may be gained by the emergent larvae.

Below: Some insects eggs are vividly-colored to warn that they carry toxins.

Above: A Praying Mantis nymph—which looks like a small adult.

Right: A Burnet Moth larva, or caterpillar—which looks nothing like an adult.

Larvae

As a result of the rich variety of creatures found in the insect kingdom, the life histories of larval insects are many and varied. Often the first thing that a freshly-emerged larva eats is the protein-rich egg case it came from. While most larvae are left to their own devices, some insects such as earwigs care for their young for some time. The larvae of social insects tend to be fostered by members of their nest group, and are fed on demand by attentive workers. All insect larvae are wingless, sexually immature, and are usually very small. Their capacity to grow, however, outstrips that of most other animals by a large margin. Caterpillars, for instance—the larvae of butterflies and moths—are extremely efficient feeding machines, and are capable of multiplying their body size by several thousand times in the course of a few weeks.

There are five basic forms of larvae—these are: eruciform; campodeiform; scarabaeiform; elateriform; and vermiform. An eruciform larva has the body shape of a caterpillar, and as such is most often seen in butterflies and moths. Campodeiform larvae are flattened crawlers with stout bodies like those of ladybugs or stoneflies. Scarabaeiform larvae are white grubs, such as those of wood-boring beetles. Larvae which are said to be elateriform are long and thin, and are represented by species such as mealworm beetles. Vermiform larvae have maggot-like form and no legs— these are typified by blow-flies.

With the exception of those found in most marine and frozen habitats, insect larvae exploit almost every possible food source on the planet. A very large proportion—such as those of butterflies, moths, sawflies, and many beetles—eat plant material. Others, however, including the larvae of ladybirds, lacewings, dragonflies, and carnivorous beetles prey on small animals like aphids, aquatic invertebrates, and even immature amphibians.

Most insect larvae develop into adults over the course of a few weeks; however, some of the species that live in temperate zones may over-winter as larvae before pupating. Although the typical lifespan of an insect is measured in weeks or months, there are several large groups that live for much longer periods. The larger dragonflies may remain as larvae for up to five years. This is far exceeded by some cicadas, however, which take seventeen years to make the transition from egg to adult.

Many insect larvae are covered with long toxin-carrying hairs—these help protect them against both predators and parasites.

The grasshopper nymph in this photo blends into its background so well that it is difficult to see...

But shows up more clearly when resting on a flower.

Pupae

When the larva has reached full growth, it changes into a pupa. Often this transition will be preceded by a search for a safe refuge where it can pass through this often vulnerable part of its life-cycle with the minimum risk. The larvae of many insect species—for example, the caterpillars of some moths—will wander for relatively large distances in a seemingly random fashion before pupating. This enormous expenditure of energy on dispersal makes sense from a survival perspective, though, as it helps minimize the risk of predation or being parasitized. If all the larvae from a brood were to remain near the plants they fed on, they would be easy prey.

There are three basic types of pupal form—these are obtect, exarate and coarctate. An obtect pupa has all the legs and appendages contained inside the pupal case. An exarate pupa has the legs and appendages on the outside of the pupal case. A coarctate pupa is fully contained within the larval skin. Many insects construct some form of cocoon to protect themselves from parasites and predators. Perhaps the best known is that of the silkworm, for which the larva of the *Bombyx mori* silkmoth produces an elaborate cocoon made of raw silk fibre. These protective structures are often bonded together by the larva with powerful enzyme-based glues

Butterfly pupae are usually formed hanging from a leaf or twig that is concealed amongst vegetation. Here they can develop in peace until they are ready to emerge as adults.

produced by special glands. The larva of the Alder Kitten moth, for example, chews up wood bark and then bonds it into an almost impregnable wooden case. Some pupae—notably those of certain butterfly species—feature highly reflective silver or gold-colored panels which are designed to reflect the surrounding vegetation to provide an elegant adaptive camouflage.

The length of time that an insect species remains as a pupa varies both with the species and often according to environmental circumstances. Many over-winter in this form, whereas others may take only a few days to undergo the remarkable transformation from larva to adult insect.

Many moth pupae—such as this Death's Head Hawkmoth—are formed inches underground.

Adult

Once an individual has completed its time as a pupa, it emerges as an adult. Those species with the power of flight usually have to spend some time expanding and drying out their wings before they are able to fly. The wings of insects such as butterflies and moths must be pumped full of a fluid to make them unfold properly. This liquid is known as molting or emergence fluid; however, once the wings are fully extended, it is drained back out of the wings and expelled. While this process is underway, the insects' exoskeletons also harden.

While many adult insects are adapted to feed on various food sources, many do not have any mouthparts, and have to survive on fat reserves laid down during the larval stage. These include many of the larger species such as the Titan beetle and Atlas moths. Most adult insects do not survive for more than a few weeks. However, some butterflies, such as those in the Heliconius genus, have evolved to synthesize proteins

False eyes are a common feature of butterfly wing patterns. These act to confuse predators.

from pollen. This allows them to live for far greater periods, and a lifespan of up to eight months is common. One of the reasons these creatures are able to stay alive for so long is that they are highly toxic, and have bright markings on their wings to warn potential predators to stay away. They also have long memories, and so are able to navigate their way around hazards and return to good food sources time and again. At the other end of the scale, many insects that are aquatic as larvae have incredibly brief lives as adults. The mayflies exemplify this situation, and usually only live for a few hours—which is just long enough to mate and then lay their eggs.

The cockroach has changed little since the early Cretaceous period, some 145 million years ago.

Evolution

Insects evolved a long time ago, but exactly when and how this came about is still not clearly understood. There are fossil remains that suggest the first species probably arose in the Devonian era, between 360 and 416 million years ago. Insects did not begin to flourish until the Late Carboniferous period, however—possibly due to fluctuating levels of atmospheric oxygen. Since insects do not fossilize well, examples from this early era are few and far between. There are excellent specimens preserved in amber from the Lower Cretaceous period, but these are more recent by some 200 million years. Due to the paucity of direct evidence, little is known about how the first insects developed, or when their flight first evolved. Among these early pioneers of the sky were giant dragonflies which had wingspans of up to 28 in (70 cm), making them far larger than any insects alive today. There are probably two main reasons why they were able to grow to such sizes back then: firstly, current atmospheric oxygen levels are too low to sustain such large body sizes; and secondly, these insects had no aerial predators to contend with. Birds did not evolve until much later.

Over the course of geologic history, various insect orders flourished and then died out, with many of them disappearing during the Permian-Triassic extinction event, around 252 million years ago. Some established themselves successfully, however, with the Hymenopteran order—the bees, wasps, and ants—first appearing around 145 million years ago. The groups of insects we see today mostly evolved during the Cenozoic, which began around 65 million years ago. Many of them did so in conjunction with the development of flowering plants, in a process called coevolution. As a result of the close associations that became established during this time, many plants and insects now depend on each other for survival. If one becomes extinct, so does the other. Examples include situations in which only one species of insect is able to pollinate a particular plant—without its seeds being fertilized, the plant cannot reproduce and soon dies out. This is an issue that is of particular concern in places where rampant deforestation is taking place, for without understanding the full interdependence between plant and animal species, we have little chance of saving many of the valuable habitats that are being destroyed around the world.

Communication

Insects communicate in a variety of different ways. Some, such as certain beetles in the order Lampyridae, are able to send reproductive signals to each other at night with light generated by bioluminescence. This is created by special light-emitting organs; the best known examples of insects with this ability are fireflies and glow-worms. The color of light they produce varies

The female Vaporer Moth has no wings, so instead of flying off to find mates, she calls them in using a powerful pheromene scent.

The female Emperor Moth vibrates her wings to scare predators with her fearsome eyespots.

between species, and may be anywhere from green to red or yellow. Some flash their signals on and off rapidly, whereas others like the glow-worm leave their light displayed for quite long periods. Should danger threaten, however, they are able to switch the light off very quickly. There are over 2,000 species of fireflies around the world, and among them there are many different display routines. Some, for instance, synchronize their flashing so that large numbers of individuals all flash at the same time. Others copy the flashing patterns of smaller species and lure luckless males to within range and then eat them. Although glow-worms only produce light as adults, fireflies also do so as larvae—it is thought that this is a warning signal to potential predators that they contain toxins.

The masters of long-distance communication in the insect world are found amongst the moths. The females of many species are able to attract males from considerable distances using special chemical sex attractants known as pheromones. There are records of female Emperor Moths (*Saturnia pavonia*), for instance, calling in males from ranges of ten miles or more. It is thought that this feat is accomplished by smell. However, research continues into what may prove to be a much more complicated mechanism.

Many insects use visual signals to communicate with one another, although the messages that are conveyed can vary tremendously. Some insects use these messages to attract mates, whereas others use them to warn other members of the same species that they are trespassing on an established territory. This is the case with lots of dragonflies and butterflies. In many tropical regions, insects abound, and so it is vital that the numerous different species are able to distinguish between one another. As a consequence of this, all manner of visual messages are created—some rely on the way in which the wings are moved, whereas others are dictated by wing shape, color, and patterns. Ritual displays are commonplace, and are often used by females to determine which males are the fittest partners. Many flies engage in elaborate wing flicking displays.

The use of sound as a communication system is probably best exploited by certain hemipterans (cicadas) and many orthopterans, including crickets and grasshoppers. Other less obvious examples include some beetle and ant species. The process of making these sounds is known as "stridulation"—they are made when specially adapted body parts are rubbed together. The purpose of the sounds varies; often they are made to attract a mate, but sometimes they are designed for marking territories. Ants use sound signals to communicate various messages between individuals, and sometimes make them as a warning to potential intruders.

Crickets communicate with sound by rubbing parts of their body together.

Locomotion

Insects move in different ways at different stages in their life-cycles; as eggs they are incapable of movement, but as larvae they are generally highly mobile. The species which have legs can cover considerable distances—ants are a good example. Those insects which do not have legs, such as maggots, are only able to move by wriggling, which significantly restricts the ground they can cover. Most adult insects can walk to a certain extent, although exceptions include the queens of some species of Hymenopterans, which can be so large that they are incapable of moving without assistance. Typically, adult insects have six legs and walk in what is called a "tripedal gait," in which at any given time

The Stag Beetle has a six-legged "tripedal gait," in common with many other insects.

two legs on one side and one on the other are always in touch with the ground. This is a very efficient system, as it provides great stability at the same time as a fast pace. Some of the faster insects have developed special gaits for high speed maneuvers—cockroaches, for instance, actually run on two legs when they are moving at top speed. Not all adult insects develop six functional legs, however—the Nymphalidae family are known as the four-footed butterflies because two of their legs are vestigial.

Where insects live on the surface of water, they require special adaptations in order to control their movements, and surprisingly few insects have evolved to do this. The pond skater is a good example of one that is very successful in this niche. It has special water-repellent coatings on its feet. These, combined with an array of fine hairs that help to distribute its weight, allow it to walk on water without breaking through the surface film. Other insects have evolved to exploit life on the underside of the water's surface, such as the curious creatures known as water boatmen. They, like most insects that spend their lives near the surface of water, are voracious predators. When a small creature falls into the water, they quickly detect the vibrations caused by its struggles and home in and consume it.

Although life on or under the surface of water is a niche for specialists, vast numbers of insect species live in water for some or all of their lives. In order to do this, they

The Pond Skater has evolved so that it can walk on water without breaking the surface.

generally have special physical adaptations. These may range from the development of gills in the juvenile stages through to the use of water-repellent coatings or breathing structures. The larvae of some hoverfly species have long breathing tubes that allow them to breathe air whilst remaining underwater. The unusual appearance of this strange structure has led to them being known as "rat-tailed maggots."

One of the major factors in the long-term success of insects is that their ancestors were the first creatures to evolve flight. This gave them

a considerable edge over their competitors, and it was a long time before any predators were able to take to the air to chase after them. The flight mechanics of most insects are extremely complicated, with some examples such as bumblebees relying on negative pressure vortices to provide enough lift for them to be able to fly. Others, such as Atlas moths, are much more straightforward to comprehend.

Bumblebees propel themselves through the air using a highly complex flight system.

Behavior and Sociality

Most insects live their lives independently, although certain species live in social groups. These are most often found in the Hymenopterans—the bees, wasps, and ants—as well as the Isopterans—the termites. Their colonies may vary from a few individuals, as in the case of certain paper wasps species, through to tens of thousands in the larger termite colonies.

Different kinds of insects are active at different times of day. Some, such as most butterflies, need the air temperature to be relatively high before their wing muscles will work efficiently.

Consequently, they only tend to fly when the sun has risen far enough to warm the local environment. Although some moths also fly during the day, the majority fly at night —since they cannot warm themselves in the sun, they usually

The caterpillars of the Lackey Moth are gregarious, living together in their early stages.

have to vibrate their wing muscles for some time to bring them up to temperature before they can take off. Those creatures that are active during the day are said to be "diurnal," whereas those that are active at night are "nocturnal." Many, however, have evolved to function in the half-light of dusk or dawn; these are said to be "crepuscular." While daily rhythms are the most obvious, there are many others that can have a major influence on the way some insects live. Cicalunar cycles are those which are timed to coincide with the moon. Many species that experience a particularly vulnerable period in their life-cycle—such as molting or emergence—time this to occur when the moon is at its darkest in order to avoid predators. Longer cycles may be timed to work in synchronization with the seasons of the year or with annual changes. Such timing is often used by insects to trigger migratory behaviour.

Habitats

Although insects may be found in most environments, very few live in the sea, where crustaceans predominate instead. On land and in the air, however, especially in tropical regions, insects often teem in unimaginable numbers. The rainforests are home to more insects than any other habitat on Earth—one of the reasons for this is that there they can breed throughout the year. This has resulted in an incredible diversity of species, with almost every imaginable shape, color, and ecological niche being represented or exploited somewhere. Insects also do well in temperate climates, but in areas where the temperature is low, far fewer species can be found. In places where this is the case, a small number of insect species can sometimes more or less dominate the landscape. In the arctic tundra, for instance, biting flies such as mosquitoes, midges, black flies, and deer flies can be found in their billions. Their bites are so painful that few creatures can withstand their onslaughts, and many migrate away from the area until after their flying season has ended. Like everything else that lives in such a harsh environment, these insects have all evolved special low temperature adaptations.

The larva of the Crane Fly is a significant pest of backyards and fields, where it feeds underground on the roots of various plants, often in large numbers.

Deserts are also tough places for insects to live, and in the more extreme areas, the lack of moisture prevents all but a hardy few from surviving. The Namib Desert beetle (*Stenocara gracilipes*), is a good example of an insect that lives in a particularly arid region. In order to be able to sustain itself, this small beetle has evolved a special coating on its wing cases with minute structures in it to catch atmospheric moisture from the mists that form at daybreak.

Human-Insect Interaction

Insects play an enormous part in the environment—without them, the world would simply cease to exist in the form we know it. Most flowering plants depend on insects like bees and butterflies to pollinate them, and could not reproduce on their own. The soil they grow in is largely created by the actions of insect larvae, and if it were not for the decomposition role played by countless billions of others, the world's landmass would be covered with dead and dying matter. From a human's perspective, insects can be both good and bad. Some of the most serious diseases in the world are spread by creatures like mosquitoes, tsetse flies, fleas, and lice.

Termites are an incorrigible pest of homes and backyards in many places.

Others, such as weevils and cockroaches, get into our stores and consume our food supplies. Colorado beetles can wreak havoc with potato crops, and locusts can devastate vast areas of agricultural land. Wood boring insects such as termites can do immense harm to our homes. Beneficial insects make honey, produce silk, prey on pests, and, as we have seen, pollinate our crops. Consequently, it is important that we learn which species are helpful and which should be avoided.

The fearsome looking Praying Mantis is a ruthless predator which feeds on numerous other insects—and sometimes even small reptiles and birds.

Insect Predators

By far the most efficient insect predators are other insects. These include the praying mantids, parasitic wasps and flies, carnivorous hornets and beetles, aerial dragonflies, and many kinds of water bugs. Outside the insect kingdom, many animals are extremely well adapted to hunt and eat them also. Among the vertebrates, this includes everything from mice to hedgehogs, anteaters, monkeys, reptiles, amphibians, and, of course, birds. Invertebrate predators include spiders, scorpions, centipedes, millipedes, and others. One of the most insidious of all natural control systems, however, are various kinds of fungus—these find their way into the breathing tubes of many kinds of insects and kill them from within.

Conservation

In spite of all the media attention directed at reducing the amount of deforestation and other environmental damage, large numbers of animals and plants are still being made extinct. No-one knows how many insects are included in this toll, and so it is vital that conservation efforts are maintained. Habitat loss is by far the biggest problem, and although many governments pass new laws to protect their natural environments, few actually enforce the regulations

Insects live in every part of the world and play a vital role in keeping the environment in balance and the Earth as we know it. They are an essential part of a healthy ecosystem.

adequately. As individuals, the best thing we can do is to ensure that whatever land we have access to is managed in an insect-friendly manner. If everyone with a garden made the effort to provide food and shelter for wild creatures, the whole ecosystem would benefit. To this extent, it is important to gain a thorough understanding of what will and will not help. For example, hiding a patch of nettles "for the butterflies" behind a shed or in a shady corner may appear to be a significant gesture, but in fact most of the species that feed on them are very particular about where the plants are situated. If they are not in a sufficiently well-lit and ventilated location, any larvae would quickly succumb to fungal infections. Consequently, Small Tortoiseshells, Peacocks, and other nettle-feeding species will not lay their eggs on them. It would be far better to use an area as a safe insect over-wintering zone by stacking some old logs in a position where they will not get disturbed. Establishing a pond is an even better idea, although stocking it with fish will result in any insects being eaten before they can make it to adulthood. There is a lot of information about specific conservation measures to be found in books, magazines, and on the internet, as well as with local natural history and gardening societies. At the end of the day, our planet's environment is under extreme pressure, and its wild spaces need all the help they can get!

NAMING AND TAXONOMY

All the documented insect species have a scientific name that is composed of two main parts. This is called the binomial classification or binomial nomenclature system. Although two-part naming had been in use for some time, it was first properly established by the great Swedish botanist and scientist Carolus Linnaeus in the eighteenth century, who is now known as the "father of modern taxonomy." It has been developed and revised continuously since then. Every named organism fits into a strict hierarchy that runs from the Kingdom (the highest level), through the Phylum, Class, Order, Family, Genus, and finally, Species. There are several different naming conventions within this regime, each with its own variations. Alongside the scientific names, many insects also have common names. These should only be used with caution, however, as the same names are often used for different species, depending on which country you are in. As an example, let us examine a simplified version of the classification of the Swallowtail butterfly, *Papilio machaon*; it is listed as:

Kingdom: Animalia
Phylum: Arthropoda
Class: Insecta
Order: Lepidoptera
Family: Papilionidae
Genus: Papilio
Species: *Papilio machaon* (Linnaeus, 1758)

This means that it was described for science by Linnaeus in 1758, that it belongs to the Iphiclides genus, which belongs to the Papilionidae family (the swallowtails), which in turn are in the Order Lepidoptera (the butterflies and moths), in the Class Insecta (the insects), the Phylum Arthropoda (arthropods), and the kingdom Animalia (the animals). This standard naming system has been used throughout this book.

BUTTERFLIES

CLASS: INSECTA ORDER: LEPIDOPTERA
(UNRANKED) RHOPALOCERA
DISTRIBUTION: WORLDWIDE SIZE: ½–12 IN (12.5–300 MM)

Butterflies are important pollinators of plants, and therefore play an important role in the environment. They are holometabolous insects—that is, they go through a full metamorphic life cycle composed of four distinct stages—the egg, larva, pupa, and imago (adult). They are part of the order Lepidoptera, and are made up of around 17,500 different species. These are split into three superfamilies – the Hedyloidea (the moth-butterflies), the Hesperioidea (the skippers), and the Papilionoidea (all other butterflies).

Most butterflies are brightly colored and diurnal (day-flying); however, the picture is complicated by the Hedyloidea, which are a small group of insects that in many ways bridge the gap between moths and butterflies. The skipper butterflies, of which there are about 3,400 species, also have many moth-like characteristics, such as the shape of their antennae and the form of their stocky bodies. Distinguishing between similar species of skippers can be extremely difficult, and often requires the skills of an experienced taxonomist.

MONARCH
Danaus plexippus

The Monarch is one of the best known butterflies of North America, with its annual migrations being the subject of countless documentaries. Its range, however, is almost global, with native populations in both North and South America, as well as Australia, New Zealand, and parts of the Iberian Peninsula. It has, on occasion, even crossed the Atlantic to reach the British Isles. The larval foodplants are members of the Milkweed family (*Asclepias spp*), and it is from these that the caterpillars synthesize toxic chemicals that make them highly unpalatable to birds. Female monarchs have darker veins on their wings, and the males have a spot in the center of each hindwing from which pheromones are released.

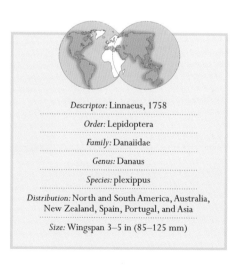

Descriptor: Linnaeus, 1758

Order: Lepidoptera

Family: Danaiidae

Genus: Danaus

Species: plexippus

Distribution: North and South America, Australia, New Zealand, Spain, Portugal, and Asia

Size: Wingspan 3–5 in (85–125 mm)

LARGE SKIPPER *Ochlodes venata*

Descriptor: Bremer & Grey, 1852

Order: Lepidoptera

Family: Hesperiidae

Genus: Ochlodes

Species: venata

Distribution: Europe and across Asia to China and Japan

Size: Wingspan: 1–1½ in (30–35 mm)

A common butterfly with an orange coloration, the Large Skipper is distributed across most of Europe and Asia. It favors places where long grasses are found, including rough pastures, moorland, and along the edges of roads as well as clear areas in woodlands and forests. Male Large Skippers are most often found perching in a prominent, sunny position, usually on a large leaf at a boundary between taller and shorter vegetation, awaiting passing females. Females are less conspicuous. Large Skippers are often seen feeding from flowers or basking in the sun. Their caterpillars feed on various grasses and other similar plants.

Pelopidas thrax MILLET SKIPPER

The Millet Skipper is found across much of south-eastern Europe, northern Africa, and southern Asia, as well as the Indonesian islands. It has also been introduced to Hawaii. It is distinguished, like most members of the Hesperiidae family, by its wide head and the wide separation of its antennal bases. This small brown or orange butterfly gets its common name from its darting, bouncy flight. Over most of its range it is a harmless addition to the local fauna, but in some areas of the world it is a major agricultural pest. This is because its larvae do tremendous amounts of damage to banana crops. In India it can be a problem where rice is grown.

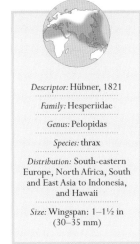

Descriptor: Hübner, 1821

Family: Hesperiidae

Genus: Pelopidas

Species: thrax

Distribution: South-eastern Europe, North Africa, South and East Asia to Indonesia, and Hawaii

Size: Wingspan: 1–1½ in (30–35 mm)

BROWN ARGUS *Aricia agestis*

Descriptor: Denis & Schiffermüller, 1775

Family: Lycaenidae

Genus: Aricia

Species: agestis

Distribution: Across Europe, north to Scandinavia; Asia as far as Siberia; North Africa

Size: Wingspan: 1–1¼ in (22–30 mm)

The Brown Argus is distributed across most of Europe and Asia as well as parts of northern Africa. Although it is a close relation to several blue butterflies, it does not have any blue markings on the upper sides of its wings, only on its undersides. It can be seen flying from early spring to late fall, especially over calcareous ground such as chalk downland and where limestone occurs. The larvae of this species feed on a variety of plants including Common Rockrose (*Helianthemum nummularium*), Common Stork's bill (*Erodium cicutarium*), and various members of the Geranium family. Indeed, they can be a troublesome garden pest in many areas.

Callophrys rubi GREEN HAIRSTREAK

The Green Hairstreak is one of a very few temperate zone butterflies to have green wings. Although it is widely distributed across Europe and Asia, as well as in parts of North Africa, it is quite local. It favors heathland, open grassland, and moorland areas, where its larvae feed on a variety of plants including Gorse (*Ulex europeaus*), Broom (*Cytisus scoparius*), Common Rockrose (*Helianthemum nummularium*), and Common Bird's-foot-trefoil (*Lotus corniculatus*). Males and females look similar and are most readily told apart by their behavior: rival males may be seen in a spiraling flight close to shrubs, while the less conspicuous females are more often encountered while laying eggs.

Descriptor: Linnaeus, 1758

Order: Lepidoptera

Family: Lycaenidae

Genus: Callophrys

Species: rubi

Distribution: Across Europe and Asia to Siberia; North Africa

Size: Wingspan: 1–1½ in (25–35 mm)

HOLLY BLUE *Celastrina argiolus*

Descriptor: Linnaeus, 1758

Order: Lepidoptera

Family: Lycaenidae

Genus: Celastrina

Species: argiolus

Distribution: Across Europe and Asia to Japan; North Africa; North America

Size: Wingspan: 1–1½ in (25–35 mm)

The Holly Blue is widespread across most of the northern hemisphere, but is more common in some years than others—which is probably due to a cyclical relationship with a parasitic wasp. The butterfly emerges early in the spring, when it can often be seen flying around areas where holly and ivy bushes can be found. It is easily identified when it first appears each year, as it emerges well before other blue butterflies. The larvae mainly feed on the leaves and buds of holly and ivy, although they will also eat a variety of other plants including gorse and bramble.

Lycaena phlaeas SMALL COPPER

A frequent visitor to gardens, where it searches for nectar-bearing flowers, the Small Copper occurs across much of the northern hemisphere in a wide variety of other habitats from open heath to grasslands to coastal systems, parks, and fields. Males like to bask in the sun in prominent positions, waiting for females to appear; should a rival male encroach on this territory, however, they will chase the intruder off. Small Coppers have even been recorded chasing away small birds! The larvae of this butterfly feed on various Rumex species including sorrel and dock.

Descriptor: Linnaeus, 1761

Order: Lepidoptera

Family: Lycaenidae

Genus: Lycaena

Species: phlaeas

Distribution: Across Europe and Asia to Japan; North Africa; North America

Size: Wingspan: 1–1½ in (25–35 mm)

COMMON BLUE
Polyommatus icarus

A small to medium-sized butterfly which is found in dry grassy areas across most of Europe, as well as parts of North Africa, and Asia. The males have a bright blue coloration on their wings and are instantly recognizable, but the females usually have a much duller mix of browns and blues, with the latter normally confined to a few scales near the body. However, these colors tend to be highly variable, even within local populations. The larvae of the Common Blue feed on a variety of low-growing herbaceous plants with Common Bird's-foot-trefoil (*Lotus corniculatus*), and Greater Bird's-foot-trefoil (*Lotus pedunculatus*) being the most commonly used.

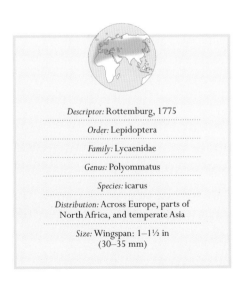

Descriptor: Rottemburg, 1775

Order: Lepidoptera

Family: Lycaenidae

Genus: Polyommatus

Species: icarus

Distribution: Across Europe, parts of North Africa, and temperate Asia

Size: Wingspan: 1–1½ in
(30–35 mm)

BROWN HAIRSTREAK
Thecla betulae

The Brown Hairstreak is distributed across most of the southern and central parts of Europe. Although it is relatively common, it can be hard to find, as it spends most of its time flying in close proximity to the upper parts of ash trees. It will, however, occasionally visit gardens to feed on flowering plants such as buddleia. It favors areas of woodland where its larval foodplant can be found; the larvae feed on blackthorn and other Prunus species. The males tend to congregate at a "master" tree while the females, once fertilized, wander widely to lay eggs. The female tends to crawl through the undergrowth, rather than fly, which again can make spotting this butterfly quite difficult.

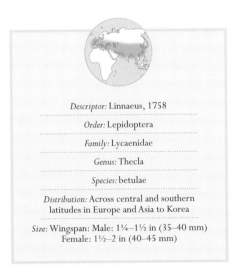

Descriptor: Linnaeus, 1758

Order: Lepidoptera

Family: Lycaenidae

Genus: Thecla

Species: betulae

Distribution: Across central and southern latitudes in Europe and Asia to Korea

Size: Wingspan: Male: 1¼–1½ in (35–40 mm)
Female: 1½–2 in (40–45 mm)

SMALL TORTOISESHELL
Aglais urticae

A common butterfly which is found across most of Europe and Asia. It over-winters as an adult—often in quiet, undisturbed places in houses and outbuildings —and is usually one of the first species to be seen flying on sunny days in early spring. The males establish transitory territories and can often be seen spiraling up into the sky to challenge would-be intruders and rivals. The larvae feed on nettles; when the eggs first hatch, the young form small communal groups protected by silken nets. As they grow, they move away from one another to feed in isolation. Once fully-grown, they hang themselves from the underside of a convenient nettle leaf and molt into a pupa, emerging as an adult a week or so later.

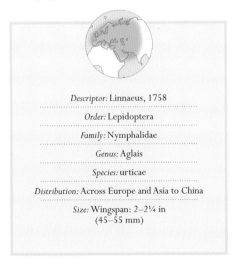

Descriptor: Linnaeus, 1758

Order: Lepidoptera

Family: Nymphalidae

Genus: Aglais

Species: urticae

Distribution: Across Europe and Asia to China

Size: Wingspan: 2–2¼ in
(45–55 mm)

DARK GREEN FRITILLARY

Argynnis aglaja

The Dark Green Fritillary is a large species inhabiting open grasslands that is widely distributed across Europe and Asia. It has a powerful flight, and in its favored localities can often be seen feeding from a variety of nectar-rich flowers. It has beautifully marked wings—these have an orange background with a network of thin black lines across them. There are several similar species of fritillary, and so obtaining a positive identification can be difficult unless a clear sighting is made. The larvae feed on various members of the violet family.

Descriptor: Linnaeus, 1758

Order: Lepidoptera

Family: Nymphalidae

Genus: Argynnis

Species: aglaja

Distribution: Across Europe to the Arctic Circle, and eastward over Asia as far as Japan

Size: Wingspan: 2¼–2½ in
(58–68 mm)

SILVER-WASHED FRITILLARY *Argynnis paphia*

Descriptor: Linnaeus, 1758

Family: Nymphalidae

Genus: Argynnis

Species: paphia

Distribution: Across Europe to Finland in the north; North Africa, across Asia to Japan

Size: Wingspan: Male: 70–75 mm (2½–3 in); Female: 2½–3¼ in (72–80 mm)

The Silver-washed Fritillary is a spectacular butterfly, especially when it is freshly emerged and still has the silver sheen on its wings. It is found across most of Europe and Asia, as well as in parts of North Africa. It has a characteristic swooping flight, and is best viewed when it settles to feed. Although the butterfly is seen mostly in sunny glades and rides, it actually breeds in the shadier parts of adjacent woodland. In some parts of Europe, a small proportion of females have wings that are bronze-green, and these are known as the form valezina. This butterfly will visit gardens and parks if suitable flowering plants are available. The larvae feed on Common Dog-violet (*Viola riviniana*) which grows in shady places in woodland areas.

Euphydryas aurinia MARSH FRITILLARY

Found in isolated pockets across much of Europe and Asia, the Marsh Fritillary is a very distinctive butterfly. Sadly, it is particularly sensitive to environmental changes, and its numbers are decreasing throughout its range. It breeds on open grassland areas where there is damp soil. Consequently, when land is drained for agricultural or commercial purposes, it can no longer survive there. The primary larval foodplant is the Devil's Bit Scabious (*Succisa pratensis*), although in some areas Field Scabious (*Knautia arvensis*) and Small Scabious (*Scabiosa columbaria*) are also eaten. After hatching, the larvae gather together in conspicuous webs until they are nearly fully grown; they then become solitary before pupating.

Descriptor: Rottemburg, 1775

Superfamily: Papilionoidea

Family: Nymphalidae

Genus: Euphydryas

Species: aurinia

Distribution: Across Europe to Asia as far as the coast of Korea

Size: Wingspan: 1½–2 in (30–45 mm)

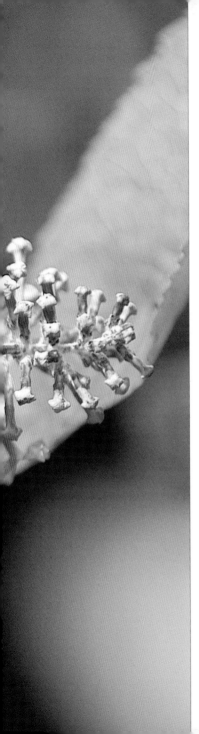

PEACOCK
Inachis io

With its vivid eyespots, the Peacock is one of the most easily recognized butterflies throughout its range. It is distributed across most of Europe and Asia. When it is at rest, its dark underwings allow it to blend in with the shadows; however, should it be startled by a potential threat, it will flash its wings open briefly, exposing the eyespots. This is often more than enough to deter the would-be assailant. The larvae feed on nettles and hops, with the first instars living in small communal groups in and around silken nets. As they mature, they move off to feed on their own.

Common name: Peacock

Scientific name: Inachis io

Descriptor: Linnaeus, 1758

Family: Nymphalidae

Genus: Inachis

Species: io

Distribution: Across central & northern Europe as far north as Finland; across Asia to Japan

Size: Wingspan: Male: 2–2½ in (62–70 mm) Female: 2½–3 in (68–75 mm)

COMMA *Polygonia c-album*

Descriptor: Linnaeus, 1758

Order: Lepidoptera

Family: Nymphalidae

Genus: Polygonia

Species: c-album

Distribution: Europe, North Africa and across Asia to Japan

Size: Wingspan: 2–2¼ in (45–50 mm)

Widely distributed around the world, the Comma is a spectacular looking butterfly that resembles a dead leaf when its wings are closed. It is named after the small comma-shaped marking that is found on the underside of the hindwings. There are two forms—the brood that emerges in early summer has bright markings, whereas the individuals that emerge a few weeks later have darker coloration. The larvae, which have a distinctive white marking along their backs, feed on various species of elm, as well as nettles and hops.

Vanessa cardui PAINTED LADY

The Painted Lady is a long-distance migrant butterfly that is distributed across most of the world, with the exception of South America. It can often be seen in gardens and parks, feeding from cultivated flowering plants. When it first emerges, it has a beautiful flesh-pink hue; however, sadly this fades after a few days. The larvae of this species are usually found feeding on nettles or thistles, although they will sometimes feed on various other plants if their favorites are not available.

Descriptor: Linnaeus, 1758

Family: Nymphalidae

Genus: Vanessa

Species: cardui

Distribution: Europe, Asia, Africa, Australia and North America

Size: Wingspan: Male: 2¼–2½ in (58–70mm) Female: 2½–3 in (62–75mm)

BLACK SWALLOWTAIL

Papilio polyxenes

A large species of butterfly that can be found throughout the United States and southern Canada, where it mostly feeds on various members of the carrot family, including dill, fennel, and parsley. The female lays her eggs on these plants during the summer. The caterpillars, which grow to about 2 in (50 mm) in length, have vivid markings along their backs which are used to signal to predators that they contain toxins and are therefore unpalatable. This species spends the winter in the pupal stage, but may be seen flying as early as the end of April and as late as the end of October. The adult butterfly is a mimic of the Pipevine Swallowtail (*Battus philenor*), which is avoided by birds due to the amount of poisons it contains.

Descriptor: Fabricius, 1775

Family: Papilionidae

Genus: Papilio

Species: polyxenes

Distribution: Most of the United States and into southern Canada

Size: Wingspan: 3¼–4½ in (80–115 mm)

ORANGE TIP *Anthocharis cardamines*

Descriptor: Linnaeus, 1758

Order: Lepidoptera

Family: Pieridae

Genus: Anthocharis

Species: cardamines

Distribution: Across Europe as far north as Scandinavia, and east across Asia to Japan

Size: Wingspan: 1½–2 in (40–50 mm)

The Orange Tip is often one of the first butterflies to emerge in spring. The males are easily distinguished due to the vivid orange markings on their wingtips, whereas the females can easily be mistaken for Small Whites or other similar species. They range across most of Europe and Asia, where their larvae feed on a wide variety of cruciferous plants, especially Lady's Smock (*Cardamine pratensis*) and Garlic Mustard or "Jack-by-the-Hedge" (*Alliaria petiolata*).

Colias croceus CLOUDED YELLOW

The Clouded Yellow, with its distinctive yellow coloration, can be found in meadows, parks, and gardens across much of southern Europe, northern Africa, and the Middle East. In some years this butterfly migrates in large numbers, and its short life-cycle allows it to produce several broods in the course of a year. The larvae of this species feed on members of the Leguminosae family—these include various species of clover, lucerne and trefoil.

Descriptor: Geoffroy, 1785

Family: Pieridae

Genus: Colias

Species: croceus

Distribution: Southern Europe and east as far as Turkey; North Africa & Middle East

Size: Wingspan: Male: 2–2¼ (50–60 mm) Female: 2¼–2½ in (55–62 mm)

BRIMSTONE *Gonepteryx rhamni*

Descriptor: Linnaeus, 1758

Family: Gonepteryx

Genus: Pieridae

Species: rhamni

Distribution: Across Europe, northwards to Scandinavia, and east as far as Mongolia; North Africa

Size: Wingspan: 2¼–3 in (60–75 mm)

The Brimstone hibernates as an adult, often hidden amongst ivy leaves. Consequently, it is often one of the first butterflies to be seen in the spring. The males have a vivid yellow coloration, and it is as a result of this that it is named (brimstone being an old name for yellow sulphur). The females of the species have a much subtler hue, which tends towards being white. The larvae of this butterfly feed on blackthorn (which is also known as buckthorn), but are often parasitized by a particular species of wasp. This is why certain populations can vary tremendously in size over the period of a few years.

Pieris brassicae LARGE WHITE

One of several species of butterfly that are colloquially known as "Cabbage Whites." Although these butterflies add variety to gardens, their larvae are regarded as significant pests, due to the amount of damage that they inflict on certain crops. The caterpillars, which feed on most members of the cabbage family, are rarely preyed upon by birds due to the amount of toxins that they contain. In reality, the most effective population controllers are actually parasites and fungal infections. Some of these target the eggs, others the larvae. The adults are strong fliers, and often migrate over long distances.

Descriptor: Linnaeus, 1758

Family: Pieridae

Genus: Pieris

Species: brassicae

Distribution: Across Europe, North Africa and east to central Asia

Size: Wingspan: Male: 2–2¼ in (55–60 mm) Female: 2¼–2½ in (60–62 mm)

SMALL WHITE *Pieris rapae*

Descriptor: Linnaeus, 1758

Order: Lepidoptera

Family: Pieridae

Genus: Pieris

Species: rapae

Distribution: Across Europe, parts of North Africa, and eastward through Asia to Japan

Size: Wingspan: 1½–2 in (35–50 mm)

The Small White is a common butterfly that can be found in most habitats across large parts of the northern hemisphere. It is, like the Large White, an acknowledged pest of plants in the cabbage family and therefore another of the species considered to be "Cabbage Whites." These butterflies often migrate over long distances, and so local control measures are unlikely to have much effect except in the immediate term. The larvae will eat a variety of wild and cultivated cruciferous plants, especially cabbages, nasturtiums, and members of the mustard family.

Pontia daplidice BATH WHITE

A species of the Mediterranean region, occurring across southern and central Europe, northern Africa, and parts of western Asia. It can be found in fields and meadows feeding on various flowering plants through its range. It is a migratory species, although it does not travel as far north as some other members of the Pieridae family, as it cannot easily withstand the winters in central and northern Europe. The larvae of this butterfly feed on mignonettes and cruciferous plants such as Wild Mignonette (*Reseda lutea*), and Hedge Mustard (*Sisymbrium officinale*).

Descriptor: Linnaeus, 1758

Order: Lepidoptera

Family: Pieridae

Genus: Pontia

Species: daplidice

Distribution: Southern and central Europe, North Africa and parts of western Asia

Size: Wingspan: 2–2¼ in (48–52 mm)

RINGLET *Aphantopus hyperantus*

Descriptor: Linnaeus, 1758

Family: Satyridae

Genus: Aphantopus

Species: hyperantus

Distribution: Across most of central and northern Europe, and Asia as far as Japan.

Size: Wingspan: Male: 1½–2 in (40–46 mm) Female: 2–2¼ in (45–50 mm)

The Ringlet is a species of the more central and northerly parts of the temperate zone, being distributed and found from the British Isles in the west, across Europe and Asia, and as far as Japan in the east. It has a dark brown coloration, with small golden circles on its underwings, and is usually found along the edges of woods and forests, where it generally flies low to the ground, rarely leaving the cover of long grasses or low branches. The larvae feed on a wide variety of grasses.

Coenonympha pamphilus SMALL HEATH

Commonly found on heath and grassland areas across much of Europe and Asia, the Small Heath is a small butterfly marked with various shades of brown. As a result of its modest coloration, it can easily be overlooked. It usually flies low to the ground and settles with its wings closed, whereupon a small eye spot is visible on the underside of the forewing. The larvae feed on a number of species of grasses in well-drained areas.

Descriptor: Linnaeus, 1758

Family: Satyridae

Genus: Coenonympha

Species: pamphilus

Distribution: Across most of Europe to Scandinavia; North Africa, and across Asia

Size: Wingspan: Male: 1–1½ in (32–35 mm) Female: 1½–1¾ in (35–38 mm)

GRAYLING *Hipparchia semele*

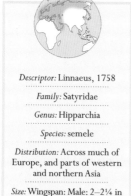

Descriptor: Linnaeus, 1758

Family: Satyridae

Genus: Hipparchia

Species: semele

Distribution: Across much of Europe, and parts of western and northern Asia

Size: Wingspan: Male: 2–2¼ in (50–55 mm) Female: 2¼–2½ in (55–62 mm)

A reasonably large butterfly of coasts, heaths, and open grassland that can be found across many of the drier parts of Europe and Asia. The Grayling is very good at camouflaging itself—when disturbed, it usually makes a short flight and then settles again, whereupon it adopts a strange slanted posture with tucked-in wings. This minimizes any shadows, which, as a result, can make it very hard to see, even from close ranges. The larvae feed on various types of grasses.

Maniola jurtina MEADOW BROWN

The Meadow Brown, which is widely distributed across Europe and Asia, is a locally abundant species. It favors areas where long grasses grow in profusion, such as heathland, coastal strips, and meadows, as well as along hedgerows and the edges of woodlands. It will often fly in overcast conditions or light rain, when most other butterflies have sought shelter. The larvae feed on a wide variety of grasses, and the adults can often be seen on nectar-rich flowers.

Descriptor: Linnaeus, 1758

Family: Satyridae

Genus: Maniola

Species: jurtina

Distribution: Across Europe as far north as Scandinavia; across Asia to the Urals and Iran

Size: Wingspan: Male: 1½–2¼ in (40–55 mm) Female: 2–2¼ in (42–58 mm)

SPECKLED WOOD *Pararge aegeria*

Descriptor: Linnaeus, 1758

Family: Satyridae

Genus: Pararge

Species: aegeria

Distribution: Across Europe, parts of North Africa, and Asia east to the Urals

Size: Wingspan: Male: 1¾–2 in (45–50 mm) Female: 2–2¼ in (48–55 mm)

The Speckled Wood is a species of butterfly found in woodland edges and clearings across Europe and Asia. The males can often be seen competing for possession of small sunlit areas in aerial combat, with both participants rising in a spiral manner until one gives up and flies off. Usually, the intruder is chased off, and the holder of the territory remains to claim any females that appear. Both sexes are superficially similar, with dark brown wings that are covered with small golden spots. The larvae feed on various species of grasses.

Pyronia tithonus GATEKEEPER

The Gatekeeper or "Hedge Brown" is distributed across most of Europe and Asia, as well as in parts of Morocco in northern Africa. It can be found along hedgerows, at the edges of fields and woods, as well as more or less anywhere that long grasses grow in profusion. Visually, it is similar to the Meadow Brown, but smaller. The larvae feed on various species of grasses, and are rarely seen. The adults often visit flowers to obtain nectar, with plants such as buddleia, bramble and thistles being especially favored.

Descriptor: Linnaeus, 1758

Order: Lepidoptera

Family: Satyridae

Genus: Pyronia

Species: tithonus

Distribution: Across Europe as far north as Scandinavia; east to Asia Minor; Morocco

Size: Wingspan: 1¼–1½ in (35–40 mm)

MOTHS

....

CLASS: INSECTA ORDER: LEPIDOPTERA

(UNRANKED) HETEROCERA

DISTRIBUTION: WORLDWIDE SIZE: ¼–12 IN (6.5–300 MM)

Like butterflies, moths are also holometabolous insects with a full metamorphic life cycle. There are around 163,000 different species, all of which are in the order Lepidoptera. This is split into two suborders—the Macrolepidoptera (larger moths) and the Microlepidoptera (small moths or "micro-moths"). There are lots of different superfamilies of micro-moths, and distinguishing between them at species level can be problematic. The larger moths, however, are generally much more easily identified. They are grouped into several different superfamilies, including the Sesioidea, Cossoidea, Drepanoidea, Geometroidea, Noctuoidea, Sphingoidea, and Uranioidea.

Although the common perception is that moths have a drab coloration, eat clothes and fly at night, many have brightly-colored wings with beautiful markings, very few actually *do* eat clothes, and some fly during the day. Some moths are economically beneficial—these include the well-known silkworm, *Bombyx mori*, from which all natural silk is derived, as well as large numbers of species that act as plant pollinators.

WHITE ERMINE *Spilosoma lubricipeda*

Descriptor: Linnaeus, 1758

Order: Lepidoptera

Family: Arctiidae

Genus: Spilosoma

Species: lubricipeda

Distribution: Across the Palearctic region

Size: Wingspan: 1½–2 in (35–45 mm)

A white-colored moth marked with delicate black spots that can be found right across the European and Asian continents throughout the summer. There is considerable variation in the degree of black speckling in this species, and some forms have the white on the forewings replaced by a yellow-ochre coloration. The White Ermine's abdomen is a bright orange color with lines of black spots—a warning to potential predators of its inedible status. The larvae will feed off almost any low-growing plants, and consequently are often found in gardens as well as in most wild habitats.

Tyria jacobaeae CINNABAR MOTH

A day flying species that was originally only found in Europe and parts of Asia. These days, however, it is distributed across most of the northern hemisphere as well as in New Zealand and Australia, as the result of deliberate introductions. These introductions were brought about by the need to control ragwort, which is extremely toxic to cattle. Since the larvae of this moth can strip a large plant in a remarkably short time, it makes for a very efficient and natural method of control. All the stages of the Cinnabar moth contain toxins, and so both the larvae and adults have bright aposematic warning colors, to deter predators.

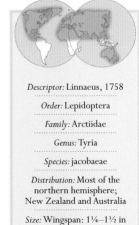

Descriptor: Linnaeus, 1758

Order: Lepidoptera

Family: Arctiidae

Genus: Tyria

Species: jacobaeae

Distribution: Most of the northern hemisphere; New Zealand and Australia

Size: Wingspan: 1¼–1½ in (35–40 mm)

PEPPERED MOTH *Biston betularia*

Descriptor: Linnaeus, 1758

Order: Lepidoptera

Family: Geometridae

Genus: Biston

Species: betularia

Distribution: Across most of the northern hemisphere

Size: Wingspan: 2–2¼ in (45–60 mm)

The Peppered Moth is distributed across most of the northern hemisphere. It is a relatively well known species, as it has been used for many years as an example of natural selection at work. The moth occurs in two main forms—a dark-colored version and the more typical light one. During the industrial revolution, trees were covered in soot, and the dark form became predominant, using the soot as camouflage, as it was harder for birds to prey on them. When the air and trees became cleaner, the light form took over once again. The larvae feed on a wide variety of trees and shrubs.

Acronicta psi GRAY DAGGER

The Gray Dagger is found in woodland throughout Europe from the Mediterranean to the northern shores of Scandinavia. The adults fly in early to mid-summer, and have a gray background coloration which is marked with dark "daggers." This moth is almost impossible to distinguish by the markings alone from the Dark Dagger (*A. tridens*). However, the larvae is unmistakable—it has red and yellow markings along the body, with a vertical projection rising from behind the neck. Its foodplants include birch (Betula), oak (Quercus), elm (Ulmus), hawthorn (Crataegus) and blackthorn (Prunus).

Descriptor: Linnaeus, 1758

Order: Lepidoptera

Family: Noctuidae

Genus: Acronicta

Species: psi

Distribution: Europe, from Spain to Finland

Size: Wingspan: 1½–2 in (35–45 mm)

ANGLE SHADES *Phlogophora meticulosa*

Descriptor: Linnaeus, 1758

Order: Lepidoptera

Family: Noctuidae

Genus: Phlogophora

Species: meticulosa

Distribution: Western Europe, from the Azores to Iceland

Size: Wingspan: 2–2¼ in (45–52 mm)

Angle Shades is a very common moth, found throughout Europe from the Mediterranean to the northern shores of Scandinavia. It has no set emergence time, and the adults can be seen at any time from early spring to late fall. The outline of this moth mimics the shape of a dead leaf, and the highly distinctive coloration is usually a suitable blend of various shades of brown, lending this species notably effective camouflage. The larvae feed on a wide variety of plants, including bramble (Rubus), oak (Quercus), birch (Betula) as well as many other trees and shrubs.

Pseudoips prasinana GREEN SILVER-LINES

The Green Silver-Lines is a common moth of woodland areas across most of Europe as far north as Scandinavia, and parts of western Asia. Its name derives from its distinctive green coloration, clearly striped with prominent lines of silver. It is a short and plump moth, with a green and silver tuft at the back of its head. The green larvae feed on oak (Quercus), beech (Fagus), birch (Betula), hazel (Corylus), aspen (Populus), as well as other trees. When it is fully grown it pupates at the end of September, overwintering in this state before emerging in late May or early June.

Descriptor: Warren, 1913

Order: Lepidoptera

Family: Noctuidae

Genus: Pseudoips

Species: prasinana

Distribution: Europe as far north as Scandinavia, and parts of western Asia

Size: Wingspan: 1¼–1½ in (32–40 mm)

IRON PROMINENT *Notodonta dromedarius*

Descriptor: Linnaeus, 1767

Order: Lepidoptera

Family: Notodontidae

Genus: Notodonta

Species: dromedarius

Distribution: Across central and northern Europe, and into central Asia

Size: Wingspan: 1½–2 in (40–50 mm)

The Iron Prominent is a common moth that is distributed across Europe and into central Asia, more or less wherever damp birch woodland occurs. The green larvae have a number of humps on their backs—it is from this feature that the name "prominent" derives. They feed on birch, alder, oak, and hazel. When the caterpillars have grown to full size in late summer, they pupate and overwinter, before emerging as adults which then fly from late spring to mid-summer.

Stauropus fagi LOBSTER MOTH

The Lobster Moth is a large species with furry legs that can be found right across the Europe and Asian continents from early to mid-summer. It is named after its strange lobster-like caterpillar which can sometimes be seen feeding on sallow (Salix), beech (Fagus), oak (Quercus), birch (Betula), hazel (Corylus), and other deciduous tree species. The larvae finish feeding by mid-fall, whereupon they pupate and overwinter until the following summer.

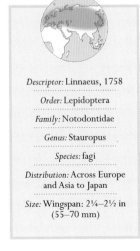

Descriptor: Linnaeus, 1758

Order: Lepidoptera

Family: Notodontidae

Genus: Stauropus

Species: fagi

Distribution: Across Europe and Asia to Japan

Size: Wingspan: 2¼–2½ in (55–70 mm)

EMPEROR MOTH

Saturnia (Pavonia) pavonia

Placed in the genus Saturnia by some taxonomists, and in Pavonia by others, the Emperor Moth has a "double" Latin name. It is a widely distributed species, ranging from Ireland right across Asia to Siberia, and from Scandinavia and arctic Russia as far south as northern Spain, the northern Alps, Slovakia, Kazakhstan, and the Caucasus. There is a subspecies of this impressive moth which can be found as far south as Morocco. The larvae, which can grow up to 3 in (70mm) in length, feed on a variety of different foodplants. Typically, they will eat birch, bramble, or hawthorn in the early stages, and then move on to heather. They will, however, happily feed on many other plants as well.

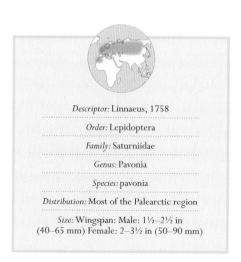

Descriptor: Linnaeus, 1758

Order: Lepidoptera

Family: Saturniidae

Genus: Pavonia

Species: pavonia

Distribution: Most of the Palearctic region

Size: Wingspan: Male: 1½–2½ in (40–65 mm) Female: 2–3½ in (50–90 mm)

DEATH'S-HEAD HAWKMOTH *Acherontia atropos*

Descriptor: Linnaeus, 1758

Order: Lepidoptera

Family: Sphingidae

Genus: Acherontia

Species: atropos

Distribution: North Africa, the Middle East, and southern Europe

Size: Wingspan: 3½–5 in (90–130 mm)

The Death's-Head Hawkmoth is distributed throughout northern Africa, the Mediterranean region, and the Middle East as far as Iran. It is, however, a migrant with a powerful flight—consequently, it can reach far beyond its resident range. This large moth has been made famous by the media due to the distinctive death's head marking on its thorax. The larvae feed on members of the potato, verbena, and olive families. Due to the shape of its proboscis, the adult is unable to feed from flowers, and often raids beehives in search of honey. When threatened, the Death's-Head Hawkmoth makes a loud squeaking noise as a deterrent.

Deilephila elpenor ELEPHANT HAWKMOTH

The Elephant Hawkmoth is a beautiful species with an unusual pink and green coloration. When it is freshly emerged, this is especially vivid, but after a day or so it fades significantly. The moth is common through much of its range, yet it is not often seen. The caterpillar of this species has distinctive eyespots on the back of its neck; if disturbed, the larva hunches it head and waves it from side to side, displaying the eyespot in an aggressive manner. This makes it look somewhat akin to a snake, and so can deter potential predators. The larval foodplants include various species of willowherb, bedstraw, honeysuckle, fuchsia, and others.

Descriptor: Linnaeus, 1758

Order: Lepidoptera

Family: Sphingidae

Genus: Deilephila

Species: elpenor

Distribution: Across southern and central Europe, and Asia to Japan. Introduced to Canada

Size: Wingspan: 2–3 in (50–75 mm)

SMALL ELEPHANT HAWKMOTH
Deilephila porcellus

As its name suggests, the Small Elephant Hawkmoth is not as large as its close relation, the Elephant Hawkmoth. It shares the same general pink and green markings, but the colors are much more vivid in this species. It is distributed across Europe and into Asia as far as Lake Baikal in Russia, and can also be found in parts of north-west Africa. The larvae feed on various species of bedstraw (Galium spp.) as well as willowherb, impatiens, and others. When fully grown in late summer, these moths pupate, emerging the following summer.

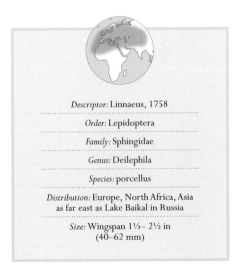

Descriptor: Linnaeus, 1758

Order: Lepidoptera

Family: Sphingidae

Genus: Deilephila

Species: porcellus

Distribution: Europe, North Africa, Asia as far east as Lake Baikal in Russia

Size: Wingspan 1½– 2½ in (40–62 mm)

HUMMINGBIRD HAWKMOTH
Macroglossum stellatarum

This hawkmoth is unusual in that it is diurnal, preferring to fly in bright sunshine. It can often be seen hovering in front of pollen-rich flowers such as buddleia, valerian, verbena, and such like. Despite its small size, it is often mistaken for a hummingbird by the uninitiated. It migrates over enormous distances, but rarely survives the winter in the northern parts of its range. This extends from the United Kingdom across Europe, and Asia as far as Japan. The larval foodplants are primarily members of the bedstraw family (Galium spp.). The larvae are green with prominent longitudinal stripes; as with the other members of the hawkmoth family, they also have the characteristic horned tail.

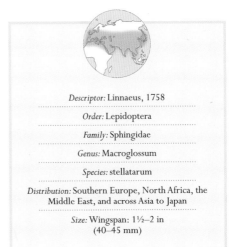

Descriptor: Linnaeus, 1758

Order: Lepidoptera

Family: Sphingidae

Genus: Macroglossum

Species: stellatarum

Distribution: Southern Europe, North Africa, the Middle East, and across Asia to Japan

Size: Wingspan: 1½–2 in (40–45 mm)

LIME HAWKMOTH *Mimas tiliae*

Descriptor: Linnaeus, 1758

Order: Lepidoptera

Family: Sphingidae

Genus: Mimas

Species: tiliae

Distribution: Palearctic region and Near East

Size: Wingspan: 2½–3¼ in (70–80 mm)

Like many of the hawkmoths, the Lime Hawkmoth is a beautiful species with a distinctive profile. The typical form is a vivid green at emergence, although this brilliance fades quite quickly. There are some genetic variants, however, in which the green is replaced by a brick red color. The larvae feed on lime (hence the name), birch, elm, and sometimes alder. When they are fully grown in late summer, they burrow into the ground and pupate, emerging the following summer. The adults lack feeding mouthparts.

Sphinx ligustri PRIVET HAWKMOTH

The Privet Hawkmoth is a large hawkmoth that is found across most of Europe and Asia. It favors woodland areas, but is often also found in urban areas. The larvae of this species, which feature seven striking purple stripes diagonally down their sides, feed on privet (*ligustri*) as well as lilac bushes and ash trees. When they are fully grown, these moths burrow into the soil and pupate, emerging the following summer. The adult has a powerful flight, with brown fore wings and pink markings on its hind wings.

Descriptor: Linnaeus, 1758

Order: Lepidoptera

Family: Sphingidae

Genus: Sphinx

Species: ligustri

Distribution: Across most of Europe and Asia to Japan. Parts of north-western Africa

Size: Wingspan: 4¾ in (120 mm)

SIX-SPOT BURNET

Zygaena filipendulae

The Six-Spot Burnet moth is widely distributed—although local—throughout Europe from the Mediterranean to the northern shores of Scandinavia. It is a day-flying (diurnal) species that can be locally abundant, especially along coastal margins. The adults—which have a dark blue-black coloration marked with six red spots—can be seen from early summer to mid-fall. This moth's flight can be somewhat clumsy, making it vulnerable in the air, but it is protected by strong toxins and is generally avoided by predators. The larvae of this species feed on bird's foot trefoil and clover.

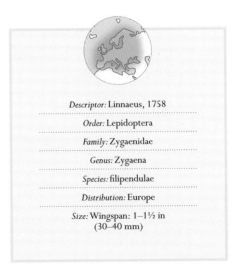

Descriptor: Linnaeus, 1758

Order: Lepidoptera

Family: Zygaenidae

Genus: Zygaena

Species: filipendulae

Distribution: Europe

Size: Wingspan: 1–1½ in
(30–40 mm)

DRAGONFLIES & DAMSELFLIES

CLASS: INSECTA
ORDER: ODONATA; FABRICIUS, 1793
DISTRIBUTION: WORLDWIDE SIZE: ½–7 IN (16–180 MM)

The order Odonata covers the dragonflies (Anisoptera) and damselflies (Zygoptera). Both have similar life-cycles, with aquatic larvae that later emerge as winged adults. In the juvenile or naiad stage, they are voracious underwater predators, hunting and eating anything that they can catch and overpower. As adults, they have two pairs of wings, and a long body. Like their larval forms, they are also fierce hunters being accomplished at catching all manner of flying insects, including butterflies, flies, mosquitoes, midges, and gnats. In order to achieve this, they have evolved large eyes which provide them with superb vision. The adult males are often very territorial, and will chase off any rivals that attempt to encroach on their domains. The males that manage to defend the best territories are those chosen by the females as mates. Once the mating process has been completed, the females lay their eggs in water —often directly into the stem of a water lily or other plant.

DRAGONFLIES

CLASS: INSECTA ORDER: ODONATA
SUBORDER: ANISOPTERA; FABRICIUS, 1793
DISTRIBUTION: WORLDWIDE SIZE: 16–180 MM (½–7 IN)

The larvae of different dragonfly species can take anywhere from six months to seven years to mature. During this aquatic stage in their development, they feed ravenously on other waterborne creatures. This includes other insects and arthropods and even small fish, as well as the tadpoles of various amphibians. They then crawl up the stem of a plant or other suitable structure where they undergo the change into an adult. In this stage they can survive for up to four months. Many dragonflies migrate long distances, and some species such as the Common Green Darner (*Anax junius*) assemble into massed groups composed of upwards of hundreds of thousands of individuals. Their powerful flight—up to 40 mph (65 km/h), allows them to travel incredible distances, and recent studies have shown that they can cover up to 85 miles (140 km) in a day.

Aeshna cyanea SOUTHERN HAWKER

Found across most of Europe from Spain in the south to southern Scandinavia in the north, and east to the Balkans, the Southern Hawker is a large species of dragonfly with a wingspan of around 3¾ in (95 mm), and a body length of 2½ in (63–70 mm). Although this species is most commonly seen near ponds, lakes, and streams, it will venture well away from water in search of insect prey. The Southern Hawker's aquatic larvae take up to three years to develop.

Descriptor: Muller, 1764

Suborder: Anisoptera

Family: Aeshnidae

Genus: Aeshna

Species: cyanea

Distribution: Throughout Europe and Scandinavia

Size: Wingspan: 3¾ in (95 mm)

HALLOWEEN PENNANT

Celithemis eponina

Also known as the "Brown-Spotted Yellow-Wing," the Halloween Pennant is quite a small dragonfly that is found near marshes and ponds in Canada, the eastern United States, and Mexico, as well as several of the Caribbean islands. The males of this species are not territorial, and they perch near the edge of ponds, waiting for incoming females. Mating typically takes place in the morning. In the more southerly parts of its range, such as Florida, this spectacular species can commonly be seen flying all year round. It has distinctive markings on its wings, which makes identification relatively straightforward.

Descriptor: Drury, 1773

Suborder: Anisoptera

Family: Libellulidae

Genus: Celithemis

Species: eponina

Distribution: Eastern North America, from Canada south to Mexico, and the Caribbean

Size: Wingspan: 1¼–1½ in (38–40 mm)

BROAD-BODIED CHASER

Libellula depressa

The Broad-bodied Chaser is found across Europe wherever there are suitable ponds and lakes. These comprise any well-vegetated still water, including backyard and farm ponds. The adults can be seen throughout the summer. As is often the case with dragonfly coloration, the males have blue bodies, whereas the females are a golden-brown color (see opposite). There are also yellow spots along the sides of the body. When freshly emerged, they have a very pale coloration, which is known as "teneral colors." It can take several days for the mature markings to develop. Mature (blue abdomen) males may sometimes be confused with males of the Black-tailed Skimmer (*Orthetrum cancellatum*).

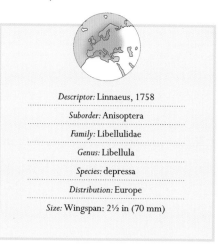

Descriptor: Linnaeus, 1758

Suborder: Anisoptera

Family: Libellulidae

Genus: Libellula

Species: depressa

Distribution: Europe

Size: Wingspan: 2½ in (70 mm)

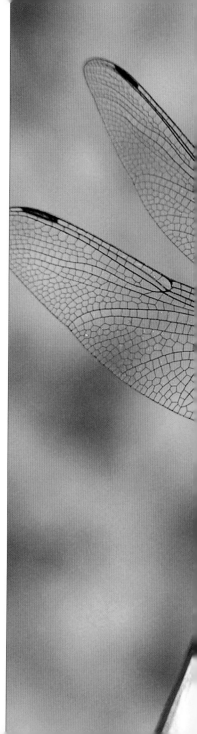

EIGHT-SPOTTED SKIMMER *Libellula forensis*

Descriptor: Hagen, 1861

Suborder: Anisoptera

Family: Libellulidae

Genus: Libellula

Species: forensis

Distribution: Western United States and Canada

Size: Wingspan: 3–3¼ in (77–80 mm)

The Eight-Spotted Skimmer is found in the western United States and the Canadian provinces of British Columbia, Manitoba, and Saskatchewan. It flies from May to August, and can be seen near ponds and lakes throughout its range. The "eight spots" cited in the common name refer to the total number of spots occurring on the wings. It has a wingspan of around 3¼ in (80 mm), and a body length of about 2 in (50 mm). Both sexes have two large dark patches on each wing, and the female has a series of yellow stripes running along the sides of its body.

Libellula luctuosa WIDOW SKIMMER

A common American species that is found across most of the central and eastern states, as well as in the Pacific Northwest, and in other isolated pockets. It can be found near ponds and lakes throughout these areas, and is often seen in parks and gardens. These dragonflies are voracious predators of flying insects, especially mosquitoes and midges. Mature males have pale patches in the middle of each wing. The brown abdomen becomes increasingly whitish as the dragonfly gets older. The eyes are dark brown to black.

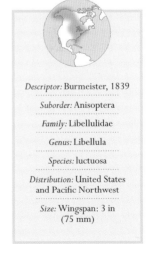

Descriptor: Burmeister, 1839

Suborder: Anisoptera

Family: Libellulidae

Genus: Libellula

Species: luctuosa

Distribution: United States and Pacific Northwest

Size: Wingspan: 3 in (75 mm)

TWELVE-SPOTTED SKIMMER *Libellula pulchella*

Descriptor: Drury, 1773

Suborder: Anisoptera

Family: Libellulidae

Genus: Libellula

Species: pulchella

Distribution: Southern Canada, United States, and Mexico

Size: 2–3¼ in (50–78 mm)

The Twelve-Spotted Skimmer is distributed throughout the United States, parts of southern Canada, and into Mexico. This attractive species is common in most regions wherever there are ponds, streams, or rivers, and the twelve wing spots—which are found on both males and females—make identifying it very simple. The males are extremely territorial, and often compete for the best locations.

Orthetrum chrysostigma EPAULET SKIMMER

The Epaulet Skimmer is distributed throughout continental Africa, as well as in southern Europe, and across Asia. It can be found in most wetland areas, as well as around ponds and lakes in drier areas. The adults prey on various flying insects, with the bodies of the males being vivid blue and those of the females a golden color. The larvae live in water as predators on a variety of aquatic creatures.

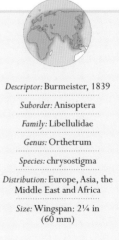

Descriptor: Burmeister, 1839

Suborder: Anisoptera

Family: Libellulidae

Genus: Orthetrum

Species: chrysostigma

Distribution: Europe, Asia, the Middle East and Africa

Size: Wingspan: 2¼ in (60 mm)

COMMON DARTER *Sympetrum striolatum*

Descriptor: Charpentier, 1840

Suborder: Anisoptera

Family: Libellulidae

Genus: Sympetrum

Species: striolatum

Distribution: Across Europe, Asia, and northern Africa

Size: Body length 1½ in (38 mm) Wingspan: 2¼ in (58 mm)

The Common Darter is distributed across Europe, Asia, and parts of northern Africa. In some years it is extremely common, whereas in others far fewer are seen. It is a strong flyer which can migrate significant distances, and can often be found around shallow ponds and lakes—indeed, it is often one of the first species to colonize new sites. The males are typically an orange to red color, with the coloration of the females being light yellow-gold. Both sexes are accomplished aerial hunters of small insects, such as mosquitoes and gnats.

Trithemis annulata VIOLET DARTER /
VIOLET DROPWING

Also known as the Violet Dropwing and the
Purple-Blushed Darter, the Violet Darter is found
across the African continent and in southern Europe.
As the name suggests, the bodies of this species have a
characteristic purplish coloration—this is only seen in
the males, however. The females are a golden color. The
males are often seen perching in a prominent location
along the edges of lakes and ponds, waiting for females
to fly by. Should a rival male enter their territory, they
will attempt to chase them off, which often results in
fierce aerial combats.

Descriptor: de Beauvais, 1805

Suborder: Anisoptera

Family: Libellulidae

Genus: Trithemis

Species: annulata

Distribution: Africa and
southern Europe

Size: Wingspan: 2¼ in
(60 mm)

DAMSELFLIES

CLASS: INSECTA ORDER: ODONATA
SUBORDER: ZYGOPTERA; FABRICIUS, 1793
DISTRIBUTION: WORLDWIDE SIZE: ½–3 IN (16–75 MM)

Damselflies are very similar to dragonflies, but, unlike their larger relatives, they are able to fold their wings along their backs when at rest. Their bodies are also far more slender, and their flight is much weaker. Where dragonflies have large eyes that more or less cover the entire head of the insect, those of the damselfly are much smaller, and usually have a gap between them. Where the hindwing of the dragonfly is typically a different shape to that of its forewing, both those of the damselfly are very similar. Although ponds and lakes are the most common places for them to spend their juvenile stage, in rainforest areas, female damselflies often find other locations to lay their eggs. These may be in water-filled plants, or in holes high in tree branches. Often these are teeming with insect larvae and so the young damselflies are assured an easy food supply.

Calopteryx splendens BANDED DEMOISELLE

The Banded Demoiselle is an eye-catching species of damselfly. The adults can often be seen flying through late spring and summer near slow-flowing rivers and streams. They occur across most of the warmer parts of Europe, Asia, and China, as well as parts of Scandinavia. The larvae live underwater for two years where they feed at night on various small invertebrates. When they have matured sufficiently, they crawl up a plant stem where they undergo a metamorphic change and emerge as an adult. The unmistakeable males, which have characteristic patches of dark blue on their wings, are very territorial and will chase off any rivals that attempt to encroach on their chosen areas. The females, however, are easily confused with the Beautiful Demoiselle.

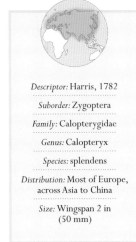

Descriptor: Harris, 1782

Suborder: Zygoptera

Family: Calopterygidae

Genus: Calopteryx

Species: splendens

Distribution: Most of Europe, across Asia to China

Size: Wingspan 2 in (50 mm)

BEAUTIFUL DEMOISELLE

Calopteryx virgo

The Beautiful Demoiselle is distributed across parts of northwest Africa, throughout Europe, and into western Asia. The males, which are very territorial, have spectacular metallic blue-green bodies with bronze-colored wings marked with blue veins. Their bodies become a darker blue color as they get older. The females are similar, but their bodies are greener than those of the males, and their wings are darker with a white patch near the tip. When they are laying their eggs—up to 300 at a time —female Beautiful Demoiselles often crawl completely underwater to find suitable places in which to deposit them.

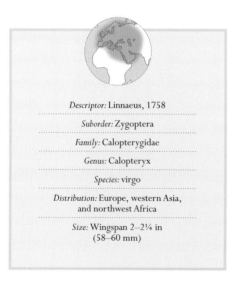

Descriptor: Linnaeus, 1758

Suborder: Zygoptera

Family: Calopterygidae

Genus: Calopteryx

Species: virgo

Distribution: Europe, western Asia, and northwest Africa

Size: Wingspan 2–2¼ in (58–60 mm)

AZURE DAMSELFLY

Coenagrion puella

The Azure Damselfly is common across lowland areas in northwest Africa, as well as Europe as far as southern Norway, and Finland. The male Azure Damselfly is sometimes mistaken for other species but can be distinguished by the characteristic black U-shaped marking which does not join up with the black ring at the posterior end of the second abdominal segment. In the female Azure Damselfly there are two color forms, blue and green. It flies between May and September, usually remaining close to fresh water. In the southern parts of its range, the aquatic larvae develop in one year; however, in the colder areas to the north, development may take as long as two years.

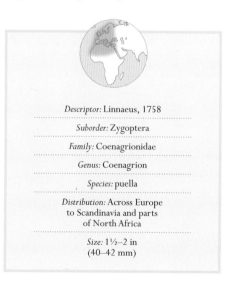

Descriptor: Linnaeus, 1758

Suborder: Zygoptera

Family: Coenagrionidae

Genus: Coenagrion

Species: puella

Distribution: Across Europe to Scandinavia and parts of North Africa

Size: 1½–2 in (40–42 mm)

COMMON BLUE DAMSELFLY *Enallagma cyathigerum*

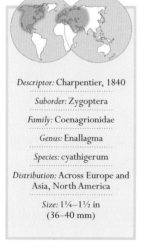

Descriptor: Charpentier, 1840

Suborder: Zygoptera

Family: Coenagrionidae

Genus: Enallagma

Species: cyathigerum

Distribution: Across Europe and Asia, North America

Size: 1¼–1½ in (36–40 mm)

The Common Blue Damselfly is found across most of the northern hemisphere, from Europe through Asia, and across the United States. It can be seen throughout the summer, especially around bodies of deep water such as large ponds, lakes, and reservoirs. The males have a vivid blue coloration, but the females can either be blue or brown. It is similar to the Azure Damselfly, but can be distinguished by careful study of the markings at the end of the tail —the Common Blue Damselfly does not have any black marking on the penultimate segment.

Pyrrhosoma nymphula LARGE RED DAMSELFLY

A medium-sized species that is common throughout Europe and Asia, the Large Red Damselfly usually stays close to water, often settling on vegetation and waterside objects. It can be found near still and slow-moving water, such as backyard ponds and small lakes. It is also able to persist on many very dry sites that have become unsuitable for other Odonata. Both sexes have striking red bodies, with the females having narrow yellow bands between the segments and black markings on the upper surface of the abdomen towards the apex. The eggs are laid on submerged plants.

Descriptor: Sulzer, 1776

Suborder: Zygoptera

Family: Coenagrionidae

Genus: Pyrrhosoma

Species: nymphula

Distribution: Across most of Europe and Asia

Size: Wingspan: 2–2¼ in (48–52 mm)

MAYFLIES

CLASS: INSECTA
ORDER: EPHEMEROPTERA; HYATT & ARMS, 1891
DISTRIBUTION: WORLDWIDE SIZE: ½–1½ IN (9–37 MM)

Mayflies are famed for their short lives as adults—
typically, they survive for less than a day in this stage.
Indeed, the meaning of the order's name "*Ephemeroptera*"
means ephemeral, or short-lived. The larval stage is aquatic,
and although it lasts a year for most species, some may take
several years to mature. They live hidden under rocks or in
vegetation in ponds, streams, and lakes, where they feed on
microscopic organisms such as algae. Emergences are usually
timed so that all the adults of a particular species appear in
one "hatch." This not only provides the best opportunities for
reproduction, but helps to reduce the losses from predation.
The numbers involved can be staggering—in some places
the air becomes thick with their weakly fluttering bodies.
There are about 2,500 species of mayfly worldwide.

STONEFLIES

CLASS: INSECTA

ORDER: PLECOPTERA; BURMEISTER, 1839

DISTRIBUTION: WORLDWIDE SIZE: ½–1 IN (9–25 MM)

Insects in the order *Plecoptera* are usually referred to as stoneflies. They have aquatic larvae which hide under stones and other objects on the beds of lakes, streams, and small rivers. Most are predatory on other aquatic invertebrates, but some also feed on vegetative matter. Stoneflies are often used as an environmental indicator—they are incapable of tolerating pollution, and so their presence in a location demonstrates that the water there is clean and free from contaminants. After the larvae have matured, they crawl out of the water, and some time later the adults emerge; they have two pairs of wings which are kept folded back over the body when they are at rest. Worldwide, about 1,700 species of stoneflies have been recorded, although the total figure may in fact be much higher than this.

CADDISFLIES

CLASS: INSECTA
ORDER: TRICHOPTERA; W KIRBY, 1813
DISTRIBUTION: WORLDWIDE SIZE: ½–1 IN (9–25 MM)

Caddisflies produce aquatic larvae that may be found in ponds, streams, lakes, and small rivers. There are three behavioral groups—one constructs protective cases, a second makes net-like structures, and the third are free-living. The case-makers spin a silken net around their bodies and then camouflage this with small debris particles such as grains of sand, small pieces of wood, and such like. They are able to move about with a reasonable degree of freedom, but if danger should threaten, they retreat inside their cases, where they become almost invisible. The net-maker caddisflies use their silken constructions to sieve food particles from the water—this includes small creatures and algae. The free-living species do not build any kind of structure, but hide under stones instead. The adult caddisflies are similar to small moths, and have two pairs of membranous wings; there are around 11,000 described species worldwide.

FLIES

CLASS: INSECTA
ORDER: DIPTERA; LINNAEUS, 1758
DISTRIBUTION: WORLDWIDE SIZE: ⅛–3¼ IN (3–80 MM)

The order Diptera comprises the true or two-winged flies—the adults have a single pair of wings, which makes them distinct from all other insects. A few are wingless, but these are all specially adapted for particular lifestyles, such as parasitism. There are a vast number of different true fly species—currently, only about 120,000 have been recorded by science, but it is thought that overall there are at least double this number. Many are agricultural or medical pests, especially the blow-flies, tsetse flies, and mosquitoes. Others, such as gnats and midges, are more of a nuisance than a serious problem. The dipteran flies all go through a fully holometabolous life cycle, with the egg being followed by a larva, then a pupa and finally the adult. The order displays an incredible amount of diversity, and the various species exploit almost every possible ecological niche on the planet.

YELLOW DUNG FLY

Scathophaga stercoraria

The Yellow Dung Fly is found across Europe, Asia, and North America from April to October more or less wherever quantities of herbivorous animal dung are found. The adult males have hairy yellow bodies, and those of the females are a yellow-brown color. They are predators on other insects, and will often sit in wait for prey on or near flowers. They mate at the beginning of spring, and the eggs are laid soon afterwards on dung, inside which the larvae develop. The adults feed on the small insects that they catch on and around the dung and the larvae feed on the dung itself.

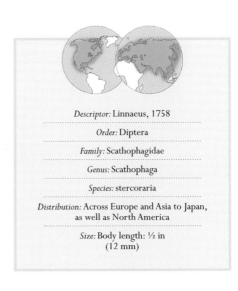

Descriptor: Linnaeus, 1758

Order: Diptera

Family: Scathophagidae

Genus: Scathophaga

Species: stercoraria

Distribution: Across Europe and Asia to Japan, as well as North America

Size: Body length: ½ in (12 mm)

BLACK SCAVENGER FLY *Sepsis fulgens*

Descriptor: Meigen, 1826

Order: Diptera

Family: Sepsidae

Genus: Sepsis

Species: fulgens

Distribution: Across most of southern and central Europe

Size: Body length: ¼ in (9 mm)

A common member of a group known either as the Black Scavenger Flies, Ensign Flies, or the Lesser Dung Flies, the Black Scavenger Fly is a small insect that is found in woodlands, along hedgerows, and in fields across most of southern and central Europe. The adult males often engage in vigorous wing waving displays to attract females. They often possess enlarged clasping organs at the base of their abdomens and on their front legs which are used to grasp the females during mating. The eggs are laid on dung, where the larvae feed and develop. In spite of their unsavory habits, Black Scavenger Flies play an important role in the environment due to the large amounts of dung that they decompose.

Tipula paludosa EUROPEAN CRANE FLY OR DADDY LONG-LEGS

The European Crane fly is known by many different local names—these include "Daddy Long-Legs" (although this is also used to refer to certain spiders), "Jimmy Spinners," and "mosquito hawks." The larvae, which live below ground eating the roots of various grasses, are generally known as "leatherjackets." Although this is primarily a European species, it has in recent years become established in North America, in parts of Canada, and the United States, where it has become a major pest. They can be found more or less anywhere that grasses grow in profusion, including lawns and parklands. The individual pictured here is a female—the sexes can easily be distinguished as the males do not have a pointed tip to the abdomen.

Descriptor: Meigen, 1830

Order: Diptera

Family: Tipulidae

Genus: Tipula

Species: paludosa

Distribution: Across Europe, Asia, the United States, and Canada

Size: Body length: 1½ in (40 mm)

ROBBER FLIES

CLASS: INSECTA ORDER: DIPTERA; LINNAEUS 1758
SUBORDER: BRACHYCERA SUPERFAMILY: ASILOIDEA FAMILY: ASILIDAE
DISTRIBUTION: WORLDWIDE SIZE: ¼–3¼ IN (3–80 MM)

Robber flies are active predators that seek out and attack other insects; more than 7,000 species have been recorded worldwide. They have long bodies and stiff spines all over their powerful legs. Although they do not fly particularly fast, their flight is powerful enough to allow them to carry sizeable prey. This may be anything from grasshoppers to spiders to butterflies—once captured, the victim is bitten with a sharp proboscis and injected with a saliva that contains a nerve poison that quickly causes paralysis. Immediately after this, powerful digestive enzymes begin to break down their internal tissues. While this is happening, they are carried off to a quiet spot where they can be consumed in safety. This is done by sucking out the resultant liquid meal via the hollow proboscis.

HOVERFLIES

CLASS: INSECTA ORDER: DIPTERA; LINNAEUS, 1758
SUBORDER: BRACHYCERA; SUPERFAMILY: SYRPHOIDEA FAMILY: SYRPHIDAE
DISTRIBUTION: WORLDWIDE SIZE: ¼–1½ IN (6–37 MM)

Hoverflies are beneficial insects that often mimic wasps —consequently, they are mistakenly killed by humans with great regularity. Their name alludes to the fact that as adults they can hover in a relatively fixed position for significant amounts of time. They produce maggot-like larvae which feed on a variety of different foodstuffs depending on the species. Some live amongst leaves, low-growing plants or in ground litter, whereas others are aquatic. Most of the latter live off decaying animal and plant matter. Many others live higher up on plants where they are insectivorous, seeking out, capturing and eating many different kinds of creatures, including sap-sucking pests such as aphids and leafhoppers. Adult hoverflies are also important pollinators, and so these creatures should be regarded as important allies to both gardeners and farmers. Worldwide, around 6,000 species have been recorded so far—and there are others out there.

HORSE FLIES

CLASS: INSECTA ORDER: DIPTERA; LINNAEUS, 1758;
SUBORDER: BRACHYCERA SUPERFAMILY: TABANOMORPHA FAMILY: TABANIDAE
DISTRIBUTION: WORLDWIDE SIZE: ¼–2 IN (6–50 MM)

There are around 3,000 species of horse flies worldwide. They are generally regarded as pests due to the painful bites that many of them can inflict, yet some species are important pollinators. The reason that horse flies bite is that the proteins they obtain from blood help with the development of their eggs. Consequently, it is only the females that bite—the males do not have the mouthparts needed to bite through skin, and instead feed on nectar and pollen. While mammals are the most common host species, some horse flies target birds, reptiles, or amphibians. They are equipped with excellent vision, and also use scent to locate their victims. Once they have done so, they do not simply pierce the skin and suck blood, but actually bite out pieces of flesh. They are maggot-like as larvae, and live in damp soil where they prey on other small invertebrates. In severe cases, sustained attacks can actually kill weakened animals.

MOSQUITOES

CLASS: INSECTA ORDER: DIPTERA; LINNAEUS, 1758
SUBORDER: NEMATOCERA SUPERFAMILY: CULICOIDEA FAMILY: CULICIDAE
DISTRIBUTION: WORLDWIDE SIZE: ¼–⅝ IN (6–16 MM)

Mosquitoes are well-known disease carrying pests that have thin wings, narrow bodies, and long legs. There are about 3,500 different species distributed across most of the world, and it is thought that more than five million people die every year as the result of their bites. Although they are notorious as blood-suckers, it is only the females that actually bite—blood is required for the eggs to develop properly. The males mostly feed off plant nectar, juices from fruit, or sap, and lack the mouthparts for biting. The larvae are aquatic, and most feed on micro-organisms, although some are predatory. They can live almost anywhere that standing fresh water can be found. Some species can go from egg to adult in as short a time as four days. Although the adults do not usually survive for much more than a week or so, in temperate areas they often over-winter. Most species are active at night or in the low light of evenings and dawn.

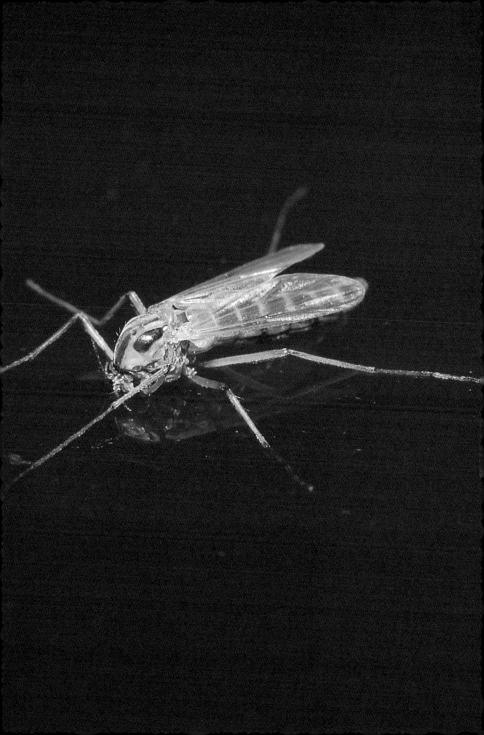

BLOW-FLIES

....

CLASS: INSECTA ORDER: DIPTERA; LINNAEUS, 1758
SUBORDER: BRACHYCERA SUPERFAMILY: OESTROIDEA FAMILY: CALLIPHORIDAE
DISTRIBUTION: WORLDWIDE SIZE: ⅜–1 IN (9–25 MM)

Blow-flies are found right across the world, with a total of around 1,100 species having been recorded. They often have metallic-blue, green, or black bodies, and since the females need to consume protein to develop their eggs properly, can be a serious problem where human food is concerned. The eggs are laid in batches of up to 200 at a time, with each female being able to produce a total of about 2,000 altogether. These usually hatch within a day, and the resultant larvae, which are generally known as maggots, typically feed on various kinds of dead or decaying matter. Depending on the prevailing temperature, they can often be ready to pupate in less than a week. At this point they leave their feeding site and burrow into the ground, emerging as adults around a week later. Many species of blow-fly create a health hazard by spreading diseases such as dysentery.

BEES, WASPS, SAWFLIES, & ANTS

CLASS: INSECTA ORDER: HYMENOPTERA; LINNAEUS, 1758
SUBORDERS: APOCRITA SYMPHYTA
DISTRIBUTION: WORLDWIDE SIZE: MICROSCOPIC—3¼ IN (80 MM)

The order Hymenoptera consists of the bees, wasps, sawflies, and ants. It is an especially numerous group, with some 103,000 species spread across 90 families. Many of them are parasitic, and the females of these species have special egg-laying structures called ovipositors which they use to place their eggs into the live flesh of their hosts. Other, non-parasitic members of the order also use them to place eggs out of danger into plant stems, tree trunks, and other relatively safe locations. The Hymenopterans are divided into two suborders —these are the Symphyta and the Apocrita. The species that make up the two groups can be distinguished by the fact that in the Symphyta the junction between the thorax and abdomen does not taper to a fine point, whereas it does in the Apocrita. All the insects that make up the Hymenopteran order are holometabolous, with the characteristic egg—larva—pupa—adult development cycle. The adults have two pairs of wings.

BEES

Class: Insecta Order: Hymenoptera; Linnaeus, 1758
Suborder: Apocrita Superfamily: Apoidea
Distribution: Worldwide Size: $\frac{1}{16}$–2½ in (1.8–65 mm)

Bees evolved many millions of years ago as the direct descendants of wasps. There are many different species —around 20,000 are known to science. They are found in every part of the world with the exception of Antarctica. Some bees are solitary, but most are social, living in large groups. The most developed bee societies are found in what are known as eusocial colonies; this designation refers to the fact that different members of the society are physiologically adapted for specific reproductive purposes. In these complex societies, the queen is the only member of the colony that lays eggs, and the majority of the population are sterile workers. Examples include the well known honey bees and bumblebees. Since they feed exclusively on nectar and pollen, their foraging activities make them one of the most important of all the flowering plant pollinators.

HONEY BEES

Class: Insecta Order: Hymenoptera; Linnaeus, 1758
Superfamily: Apoidea Family: Apidae Tribe: Apini Genus: Apis;
Distribution: Worldwide Size: ½–1¼ in (12.5–32 mm)

The honey bees—members of the tribe *Apini*—are a very small group when one takes into consideration the fact that there are around 20,000 different kinds of bees in total. Taxonomists are constantly changing their minds about which are true species and which are subspecies, but currently only seven honey bees have full species status, with a further 44 being labelled subspecies. The full species are the European Honey Bee (*Apis mellifera*), the Dwarf Honey Bee (*Apis florea*), the Eastern Honey Bee (*Apis cerana*), the Giant Honey Bee (*Apis dorsata*), and three others which do not have common names (*Apis andreniformis, Apis koschevnikovi* and *Apis nigrocincta*). It is thought that around a third of all food produced for human consumption is reliant on insect pollination, and so honey bees, which are one of the principal agricultural pollinators, are extremely significant economically in global terms.

BUMBLEBEES

CLASS: INSECTA ORDER: HYMENOPTERA; LINNAEUS, 1758
SUPERFAMILY: APOIDEA FAMILY: APIDAE TRIBE: BOMBINI GENUS: BOMBUS
DISTRIBUTION: WORLDWIDE SIZE: ½–1¼ IN (12.5–32 MM)

Bumblebees are easily recognized members of the same family as honey bees. They are, however, quite different in appearance, with furry bodies that are often marked with distinct color bands. These are usually black in color, combined with either yellow, red, or orange. They form small colonies which are typically made up of up to 50 individuals. These are often constructed in abandoned mouse holes, although some species nest above ground. Among the various bumblebee species, there are a number that are known as "cuckoo bumblebees"—these have a curious life history. The females of this group each seek out and invade a colony of bumblebees, where they kill the queen and take over the workers. She then lays her own eggs and forces the enslaved bees to raise them. Many species of bumblebee are in decline, and several have become extinct in recent years.

WASPS

Class: Insecta Order: Hymenoptera; Linnaeus, 1758

Suborder: Apocrita

Distribution: Worldwide Size: Microscopic– 2½ in (65 mm)

There are many different kinds of wasps; however, they can be divided into two main categories—those which are solitary and those which are social. They can be further sub-divided into four types—these are the Predatory, Parasitic, Social, and Gall wasps. The larvae of the parasitic wasps may feed on the eggs of other insects, or they may feed on the living tissues of various insects including butterflies, moths, beetles, or aphids, as well as spiders. The predatory wasps provide their larvae with nests filled with paralyzed prey composed of spiders or butterfly, moth, or beetle larvae. The tiny gall wasps, of which there are about 1,300 species, lay their eggs into the stems of certain plants. In so doing, they somehow manage to induce the plants to produce large swellings—it is into these that the larvae hatch. They then mature in these strange structures before emerging as adults some time later. The solitary wasps often build nests for their young—there are, however, many different types. The social wasps include the members of the Vespidae—the hornets and paper wasps —which most people are all too familiar with.

RED-BROWN OR ORIENTAL PAPER WASP
Polistes olivaceus

Descriptor: De Geer, 1773

Order: Hymenoptera

Family: Vespidae

Genus: Polistes

Species: olivaceus

Distribution: Asia, Australia,
India, Japan, United States

Size: ¾–1 in
(18–24 mm)

Found eastwards across Asia to Japan, as well as in Australia and the United States, the Red-Brown or Oriental Paper Wasp is also known variously as the Yellow Paper Wasp, Yellow Oriental Paper Wasp, and German Feldwespe. They are social insects, which build open nests made from chewed wood pulp. These are suspended from solid structures, and are often near to, or part of, human habitations. The colonies may be composed of up to 100, sometimes aggressive, individuals. These wasps can deliver a painful, poisonous sting that can affect some recipients quite seriously.

Rhyssa persuasoria GIANT ICHNEUMON WASP

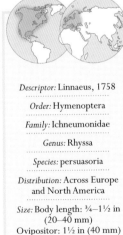

Also known as the Sabre Wasp, the Giant Ichneumon Wasp is a large parasitic insect that can be found across Europe and North America; similar species are found in most other parts of the world. They lay their eggs next to or on wood-boring larvae —mostly of wood wasps (horntails), longhorn beetles, and certain moths. Achieving this is a considerable feat, however, as the female wasp first has to drill a hole into the tree where the victim is feeding using her long ovipositor with great precision. When the eggs hatch, the wasp grubs attach themselves to the larva and start eating it. When they are fully grown, they pupate.

Descriptor: Linnaeus, 1758

Order: Hymenoptera

Family: Ichneumonidae

Genus: Rhyssa

Species: persuasoria

Distribution: Across Europe and North America

Size: Body length: ¾–1½ in (20–40 mm)
Ovipositor: 1½ in (40 mm)

SPHECID WASPS

CLASS: INSECTA ORDER: HYMENOPTERA; LINNAEUS, 1758
SUBORDER: APOCRITA SUPERFAMILY: APOIDEA FAMILY: SPHECIDAE
SUBFAMILIES: AMMOPHILINAE, SCELIPHRINAE, SPHECINAE
DISTRIBUTION: WORLDWIDE SIZE: ⅜–2½ IN (9–65 MM)

The Sphecid wasps are sometimes called the "thread-waisted wasps" because they characteristically have bodies with a very narrow junction between the thorax and abdomen. Many species within this family are known as digger wasps, because of the way they dig nest burrows. They are all both solitary and predatory, with caterpillars, spiders, grasshoppers, and cicadas being the favored prey. Some of them can be quite large—the Cicada killer wasp, for instance, may measure as much as 2 in (5 cm) in length. As its name suggests, this species seeks out and catches cicadas, whereupon the victims are paralyzed with a sting and taken to the nest site. Eggs are then laid on the hapless creature, and the whole structure sealed up with mud for protection. When the eggs hatch, they feed off the cicada's corpse until they are ready to pupate.

SAWFLIES

Class: Insecta Order: Hymenoptera; Linnaeus, 1758
Suborder: Symphyta
Distribution: Worldwide Size: ⅜–3¼ in (9–80 mm)

Sawflies first appeared around 200 million years ago, and it is from this superfamily that wasps first evolved. Adult sawflies can be distinguished from wasps by the fact that the junction between their thorax and abdomen does not taper to a fine point, whereas it does in wasps. Sawfly larvae look similar to caterpillars, and most feed on plants—either directly on leaves or by burrowing into their tissues. There is, however, one family that is parasitic. The adults are mostly carnivorous, being efficient hunters of other insects. The females of many sawflies have long ovipositors—these are used to lay eggs deep into the trunks or branches of trees. The Giant Wood Wasp is a fearsome looking creature that is actually a harmless sawfly, although due to its size and demeanor it is commonly mistaken for some kind of hornet.

Rhogogaster viridis GREEN SAWFLY

The Green Sawfly is a small predacious wasp that has a bright green coloration. It is commonly found throughout Europe in hedgerows, at the edges of woodland and in many other places where there is plenty of vegetation. The females lay their eggs directly into the stems of host plants using their specially-adapted ovipositors. These then hatch and the larvae —which look much like those of butterflies and moths —feed on the leaves of the host plant. When fully grown, they pupate and then emerge about a week later as adults. These are carnivorous on other insects.

Descriptor: Linnaeus, 1758

Order: Hymenoptera

Suborder: Symphyta

Family: Tenthredinidae

Genus: Rhogogaster

Species: viridis

Distribution: Throughout Europe

Size: ¾ in (18 mm)

HORNETS

CLASS: INSECTA ORDER: HYMENOPTERA; LINNAEUS, 1758
SUBORDER: APOCRITA SUPERFAMILY: VESPOIDEA
FAMILY: VESPIDAE SUBFAMILY: VESPINAE GENUS: VESPA;
DISTRIBUTION: WORLDWIDE SIZE: ⅜–2½ IN (9–65 MM)

Hornets are among the most feared of all insects. Folklore has it that they will attack without provocation, in spite of the fact that they are rarely aggressive. A hornet's sting is harmful, but the sting toxicity varies greatly by hornet species. Some deliver just a typical insect sting, while others are among the most venomous known insects. Allergic reactions can occur. Depending on the severity, these may result in death, but this is very unusual. There are around 20 different hornet species, all of which are eusocial. They are the largest of the colonial wasps, reaching a maximum size of nearly two inches (50 mm) in length. The nests are usually constructed out of chewed wood pulp inside a hollow tree or some other safe place. The eggs are laid in specially constructed cells, and the larvae are fed on a diet of insects. They mature in around two weeks, whereupon they pupate, emerging as adults about two weeks later.

Vespa orientalis ORIENTAL HORNET

The Oriental Hornet is found from the Middle East, through parts of Turkey and Greece, and across most of Asia. It is a very active creature, and will attack humans, but only if provoked. It is omnivorous, and will take live or dead meat, as well as fruit or any other suitable foodstuffs it can find. It can be a significant pest where it is especially numerous. This species nests in hollow trees or cavities in buildings or amongst rocks. The main distinguishing characteristic between the sexes in this species is that in males the antennae have 13 segments, while females always have only 12.

Descriptor: Linnaeus, 1771

Order: Hymenoptera

Family: Vespidae

Genus: Vespa

Species: orientalis

Distribution: Across the Middle East, Central Asia and parts of the Mediterranean

Size: Queen: 1–1¼ in (25–35 mm) Males and workers: ¾–1 in (20–25 mm)

ANTS

CLASS: INSECTA ORDER: HYMENOPTERA; LINNAEUS, 1758
SUBORDER: APOCRITA SUPERFAMILY: VESPOIDEA FAMILY: FORMICIDAE
DISTRIBUTION: WORLDWIDE SIZE: ½5–1 IN (1–25 MM)

More than 12,000 species of ants have been formally described, with the majority of these being found in tropical regions. They can be found on all the large land masses around the world, except those close to the frozen poles. They are eusocial, with their populations being split into sterile female workers, fertile male drones, and fertile females known as queens. Some ant colonies can number into the millions.

Ants often form associations with other insects, especially aphids and mealy bugs which are effectively farmed for their honeydew secretions. This relationship is beneficial for both parties, however, as in return for the sugar-rich liquids, the creatures concerned are given almost total protection from other predators. Consequently, the presence of the relevant ant species can lead to serious pest outbreaks on some agricultural crops. In many areas though, the ants that do not farm aphids are welcomed in the fields as they are extremely efficient at seeking out and killing every kind of small creature they can find and overcome.

SOUTHERN WOOD ANT *Formica rufa*

Descriptor: Linnaeus, 1761

Order: Hymenoptera

Family: Formicidae

Genus: Formica

Species: rufa

Distribution: Across Europe,
Asia, and North America

Size: ½ in
(12 mm)

The Southern Wood Ant is one of a number of very similar species that are distributed across most of the northern hemisphere—this complex of species is known to scientists as "the *Formica rufa* group." They are found in coniferous and mixed woodland, where they build large mound-like nests constructed out of dry plant matter and soil. They have close associations with aphids, and the workers tend to protect and collect honeydew from their charges. They are very aggressive, and will attack and kill any other creatures that they meet on their travels. The remains of their victims are then transported back to the nest as food.

Lasius niger BLACK ANT

The Black Ant is distributed throughout the northern hemisphere, where in many places it is the predominant ant species. In most cases, it rarely causes a significant problem and can be ignored unless large numbers make their way into domestic dwellings, when it can become a serious nuisance. In gardens, however, its presence is usually unwelcome, as it fosters aphids, protecting them from predacious insects. It will also attack various kinds of soft fruit, especially strawberries and raspberries. After mating the male ant dies and the females shed their wings and find shelter to overwinter. The females will produce eggs from late spring.

Descriptor: Linnaeus, 1758

Order: Hymenoptera

Family: Formicidae

Genus: Lasius

Species: niger

Distribution: Across Europe, Asia, and North America

Size: Workers: ¼ in (6 mm)
Queen: ½ in
(15 mm)

GRASSHOPPERS, CRICKETS, & LOCUSTS

CLASS: INSECTA
ORDER: ORTHOPTERA; LATREILLE, 1793
DISTRIBUTION: WORLDWIDE SIZE: ⅜–3¼ IN (9–80 MM)

The Orthoptera order comprises the grasshoppers, bush crickets, mole crickets, house crickets, and locusts. While they are mostly herbivorous, many bush crickets are voracious predators. They are hemi-metabolous insects—that is, they undergo incomplete metamorphosis, developing from an egg into a nymph (often known as a "hopper") that gradually grows through various instars until it is ready for the final moult. At the adult stage it has two pairs of wings, which for most of the time are kept folded together along the back. The ability to fly varies with species, from those that cannot fly, such as the Giant Weta, to accomplished fliers such as the locust. Most of the time, however, they move around on the ground, using their powerful back legs to jump often considerable distances.

GRASSHOPPERS

CLASS: INSECTA   ORDER: ORTHOPTERA; LATREILLE, 1793
SUBORDER: CAELIFERA
DISTRIBUTION: WORLDWIDE   SIZE: ⅜–3¼ IN (9–80 MM)

There are around 11,000 different species of grasshopper, distributed across some 2,400 genera. The majority of these are found in tropical regions; however, others can be found across most of the temperate zones as well. They are all herbivorous, and can vary in size from less than an inch to over six inches in length. One characteristic of the group that helps to distinguish them from other similar suborders is that they have short antennae—typically these are shorter than the body. They usually have cryptic coloration, which helps them to avoid predators—if this does not work, however, they are usually ready to make use of their powerful back legs to jump to safety. Some species use their wings to assist this process by gliding the last few feet.

Grasshoppers are well-known for making musical "chirps"—this is known as stridulation, and is achieved by rubbing the legs or wings together. The sounds they produce are mainly for reproductive purposes. Once a female has mated successfully, she usually lays her eggs in soft ground or at the base of various plants.

Chorthippus parallelus MEADOW GRASSHOPPER

The Meadow Grasshopper is a common species that is widely distributed across Europe, where it can be found more or less wherever long grass grows freely. It has a green background coloration, which is usually combined with various brown markings. There are, however, lots of variations, with red and purple being commonplace additions to the color scheme. The adults communicate with the well known grasshopper chirping sounds as frequently as every few seconds.

Descriptor: Zetterstedt, 1821

Order: Orthoptera

Family: Acrididae

Genus: Chorthippus

Species: parallelus

Distribution: Across Europe

Size: Males: ¼–¾ in
(10–20 mm) Females: ½–1 in
(15–25 mm)

BLUE-WINGED GRASSHOPPER *Oedipoda caerulescens*

Descriptor: Linnaeus, 1758

Order: Orthoptera

Family: Acrididae

Genus: Oedipoda

Species: caerulescens

Distribution: Europe; absent from the United Kingdom

Size: 1¼ in (30 mm)

Found across most of Europe, but not on the United Kingdom mainland, the Blue-Winged Grasshopper is common in many places, especially dune systems and on other arid soils. The eggs hatch in early summer, and reach sexual maturity in July. When threatened, these grasshoppers jump into the air using their powerful back legs and then glide to safety. When it takes flight its blue-hind wings are very conspicuous; the grasshopper appears like a blue butterfly for a few moments then appears to vanish as it comes to rest.

Omocestus viridulus COMMON GREEN GRASSHOPPER

The Common Green Grasshopper is distributed across Europe and northern Asia, where it can be found in a variety of grassland habitats over most altitudes. The males can be a variety of colors, but their background is usually mostly brown. The females are even more variable, and may show splashes of red or purple in their coloration. They lay their eggs in the autumn—these hatch in the spring, and the young hoppers grow through a series of instars until they reach full maturity in early summer.

Descriptor: Linnaeus, 1758

Order: Orthoptera

Family: Acrididae

Genus: Omocestus

Species: viridulus

Distribution: Across Europe and northern Asia

Size: 1–1½ in (25–30 mm)

BUSH CRICKETS

CLASS: INSECTA ORDER: ORTHOPTERA; LATREILLE, 1793
SUBORDER: ENSIFERA SUPERFAMILY: TETTIGONIOIDEA
FAMILY: TETTIGONIIDAE
DISTRIBUTION: WORLDWIDE SIZE: ⅜–3¼ IN (9–80 MM)

There are around 6,800 different bush cricket species, found in many different parts of the world. These interesting insects are also known as "katydids" in some regions. Although they look very similar to grasshoppers, bush crickets can usually be distinguished from them by the length of their antennae, which are typically longer than the body. Indeed, these creatures used to be known as "long-horned grasshoppers," due to their long, thread-like antennae, but bush cricket is actually a more appropriate name, clearly distinguishing them from their grasshopper cousins. As with the other orthopterans, the bush crickets undergo incomplete metamorphosis, progressing from egg to adult in small increments. While most species eat a variety of plant matter, some are accomplished predators, preying on anything they can catch and kill, including other insects as well as small vertebrates. Although most bush crickets have little economic significance, a few species, such as the Mormon cricket (*Anabrus simplex*), can become numerous enough to become a major agricultural pest.

Leptophyes punctatissima SPECKLED BUSH CRICKET

Commonly found throughout Europe, from the Mediterranean to southern Scandinavia, the Speckled Bush Cricket has also been introduced to the United States in recent years. It has long, powerful legs, but no wings, and is well camouflaged for its grassy environment, with a predominantly green coloration. This is marked with flecks of brown and small dark speckles. It has a high-pitched song, and although it enters backyards, is not a pest.

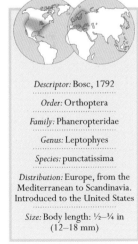

Descriptor: Bosc, 1792

Order: Orthoptera

Family: Phaneropteridae

Genus: Leptophyes

Species: punctatissima

Distribution: Europe, from the Mediterranean to Scandinavia. Introduced to the United States

Size: Body length: ½–¾ in (12–18 mm)

DARK BUSH CRICKET *Pholidoptera griseoaptera*

Descriptor: De Geer, 1773

Order: Orthoptera

Family: Tettigoniidae

Genus: Pholidoptera

Species: griseoaptera

Distribution: Across Europe

Size: Length: Males: ¼–¾ in
(10–20 mm) Females: similar,
but with ¼–¾ in (10–20 mm)
ovipositor

The Dark Bush Cricket is a wingless species that
is found in grassy habitats and on rough ground
across much of Europe. Its presence is often signaled
by the chirping sounds it makes through warm summer
days and into late evenings. This is a brief chirping
noise which is repeated every few seconds; these
calls are made both for territorial and mate attractant
purposes. The Dark Bush Cricket will keep up this
persistent song all through the night. This species eats
plant matter and small invertebrates.

Tettigonia viridissima GREAT GREEN BUSH CRICKET

A striking green insect which has a brown marking along the center of its back, the Great Green Bush Cricket is found from North Africa through Europe and Asia Minor and eastward as far as Siberia. It eats both plant matter and small creatures. The adult males generate a loud, distinctive song from midday until well after dark. The nymphs hatch in late spring and spend the first few weeks of their lives amongst low herbage. Once they have matured, they move up into the bushes and trees.

Descriptor: Linnaeus, 1758

Family: Tettigonidae

Genus: Tettigonia

Species: viridissima

Distribution: Europe, North Africa, Siberia, Asia Minor

Size: Length: Males: 1½–2 in (40–50 mm) Females: similar, but with ¾–1 in (20–25 mm) ovipositor

MOLE CRICKETS

CLASS: INSECTA ORDER: ORTHOPTERA; LATREILLE, 1793
SUBORDER: ENSIFERA SUPERFAMILY: GRYLLOIDEA FAMILY: GRYLLOTALPIDAE
DISTRIBUTION: WARM TEMPERATE TO TROPICAL SIZE: ⅜–3¼ IN (9–80 MM)

Although mole crickets are quite common, they are rarely seen as they are nocturnal creatures that spend most of their lives underground in long tunnels. They can reach in excess of two inches in length, and have very powerful front legs which are superbly adapted for digging. They have an omnivorous diet, and will eat more or less anything that they find on their travels, including worms, roots, and leaves. Where their numbers reach sufficient proportions, they can become minor pests. During the mating season adult mole crickets will fly several miles in search of a mate, and when the occasion demands, they are also good swimmers. In some areas they are threatened by habitat loss.

TRUE CRICKETS

CLASS: INSECTA ORDER: ORTHOPTERA; LATREILLE, 1793
SUBORDER: ENSIFERA SUPERFAMILY: GRYLLOIDEA FAMILY: GRYLLIDAE
DISTRIBUTION: WORLDWIDE SIZE: ⅜–2 IN (9–50 MM)

The true crickets are known to most people who live in the warmer parts of the world, mostly as the result of the chirping noises made by the males of the species. This nocturnal stridulation is made to signify territorial claims, and as a result attract mates. The family is distributed across the world in around 900 different species, including the well-known house cricket. This is, in spite of its name, actually a member of a group known as field crickets. Although crickets are superficially similar to grasshoppers, they have flatter bodies and longer antennae. The females lay their eggs in batches of up to 2,000 into damp soil or other similar places using a long ovipositor.

TRUE BUGS

Class: Insecta Order: Hemiptera; Linnaeus, 1758
Distribution: Worldwide Size: ⅜–3¼ in (9–80 mm)

The order Hemiptera is a large group of insects that is known as the "True Bugs." It includes the shield bugs, froghoppers, leafhoppers, aphids, cicadas, scale insects, mealybugs, and water bugs. In total around 80,000 species have been recorded by science, and they can be found everywhere there is land except the frozen areas near the poles. All the true bugs feed through sucking mouthparts—while some, such as cicadas and planthoppers, only ingest plant juices, many others are voracious predators. These include the assassin bugs (Family Reduviidae), of which there are around 7,000 species worldwide. The smallest true bugs may be less than 1 mm long, whereas the largest ones may exceed 4 inches (100 mm). All the true bugs are hemimetabolous, with tiny nymphs hatching from eggs. They then grow through a series of instars until they become sexually mature adults, complete with wings (if present in the species). While the vast majority of true bugs have to pair in order to reproduce, some are able to do so without mating.

FROGHOPPERS

CLASS: INSECTA ORDER: HEMIPTERA; LINNAEUS, 1758
SUBORDER: AUCHENORRHYNCHA SUPERFAMILY: CERCOPOIDEA
DISTRIBUTION: WORLDWIDE SIZE: ⅜–¾ IN (3–19 MM)

Froghoppers are small insects that can easily escape notice; however, the presence of their larval stages is more obvious, as they produce the white protective froth often referred to as cuckoo spit. They are known as "spittle bugs" in some parts of the world. The superfamily also includes a group known as tube spittle bugs. Froghoppers can be very difficult to distinguish from leafhoppers (superfamily *Membracoidea*, family *Cicadellidae*), and in many cases require very close examination with magnifying lenses.

The life-cycle of the froghopper begins with the egg which is laid on a suitable foodplant. When this hatches, the nymph quickly pierces the plant's stem and begins making the protective froth. This not only hides it from predators, but also prevents it from drying out. When it reaches the adult stage, it no longer lives in froth, but protects itself by being able to jump out of danger.

Cercopis vulnerata BLACK & RED FROGHOPPER

The Black & Red Froghopper is a distinctive species that can be seen during the summer on low vegetation throughout central and southern Europe. It is a common froghopper, and its black and red markings make identification easy. As nymphs, they feed on sap from plant roots, and as adults they suck the juices from a variety of vegetation, including nettles, grasses, and other low-growing herbage. If threatened, this insect is able to jump an incredible distance.

Descriptor: Rossi, 1807

Order: Hemiptera

Family: Cercopidae

Genus: Cercopis

Species: vulnerata

Distribution: Central and southern Europe

Size: ¼ in (9–10 mm)

SHIELD BUGS

CLASS: INSECTA   ORDER: HEMIPTERA; LINNAEUS, 1758

SUPERFAMILY: PENTATOMOIDEA

DISTRIBUTION: WORLDWIDE   SIZE: ⅛–1 IN (3–25 MM)

Shield bugs—which are sometimes called "stink bugs," due to their ability to produce an acrid liquid discharge—are hemimetabolous insects in the order of true bugs. There are over 4,700 different species of these insects, distributed across nearly nine hundred genera. Many shield bugs are vividly colored; although this makes them stand out to potential predators, it is, in fact, a stark visual warning that they contain unpalatable chemicals. This mechanism is known as "aposematic coloration." Should the warning go unheeded by a potential predator, they eject a foul-smelling liquid from special glands which usually deters the would-be attacker. The nymphs look very similar to the adults, and go through a series of instars as they grow until they undergo the final molt into adult form.

DOCK LEAF BUG

Coreus marginatus

Also known as the Brown Squash Bug, the Dock Leaf Bug is common across Europe, Asia, and North America, and can be seen in wild places and gardens throughout its range. Found on many flowers, it does not have the side stripes seen in other Shield Bug species and its shoulders are more rounded. It has two small distinctive pointers in the front of the head between the antennae which have dark tips, whilst those of the superficially similar *Arma custos* species are light-tipped. It is able to hibernate in all its stages, and so adults and young may be seen side by side, often in small groups. It feeds entirely on plant matter, from leaves to fruit. When threatened, it either releases a toxic chemical or takes flight.

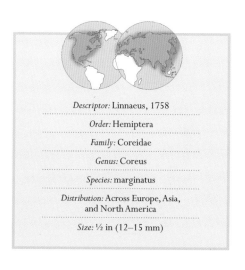

Descriptor: Linnaeus, 1758

Order: Hemiptera

Family: Coreidae

Genus: Coreus

Species: marginatus

Distribution: Across Europe, Asia, and North America

Size: ½ in (12–15 mm)

RED-BLACK SHIELD BUG *Graphosoma lineatum*

Descriptor: Linnaeus, 1758

Order: Hemiptera

Family: Pentatomidae

Genus: Graphosoma

Species: lineatum

Distribution: Across southern Europe and central Asia

Size: ¼–½ in (8–12 mm)

Also known as the Striped Shield Bug or Red & Black Striped Stink Bug, the Red-Black Shield Bug is an unmistakable insect that occurs across much of southern Europe and central Asia. It is commonly seen on flowers, especially those of the umbelliferae family such as Wild carrot, Cow Parsley, and so on. It makes no attempt to hide from predators because it has vivid red and black striped markings running from head to tail that mark it out as a creature with powerful chemical defences. On the underside the stripes are replaced with dots. The nymphs—which feed on plant juices—are brown with yellow markings.

Palomena prasina GREEN SHIELD BUG

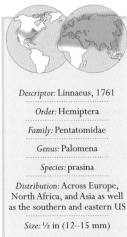

The Green Shield Bug or Green Stink Bug is found across most of North Africa and Europe, as well as the temperate parts of Asia. It also occurs in the southern and eastern parts of the United States. It is commonly seen in gardens as well as on farmland and uncultivated areas. Although this species is mostly green all the way through from nymph to adult, it turns brown before hibernating, and then turns green again about a week afterward. The eggs are laid in batches on the undersides of leaves. There are a number of other green species looking exactly like the Green Shield Bug. Most of them are not as common in Europe.

Descriptor: Linnaeus, 1761

Order: Hemiptera

Family: Pentatomidae

Genus: Palomena

Species: prasina

Distribution: Across Europe, North Africa, and Asia as well as the southern and eastern US

Size: ½ in (12–15 mm)

WATER BUGS

CLASS: INSECTA ORDER: HEMIPTERA; LINNAEUS, 1758
SUBORDER: PROSORRHYNCHA
DISTRIBUTION: WORLDWIDE SIZE: ⅛–1¼ IN (3–32 MM)

The group of creatures referred to as water bugs includes a number of aquatic insects that typically live on or under the surface-film of ponds, lakes, and streams. They are efficient hunters, and many have special sensing hairs that can detect the slightest vibrations from a small creature that has fallen into the water. When the drowning animal's attempts to struggle free are felt by a water bug, it will rapidly seek out the victim and devour it, if possible. Should several individuals be present, a fight can break out, with the largest specimen usually winning the contest. The group includes the water scorpions, water boatmen, water crickets, water measurers, and pond skaters.

Gerris lacustris COMMON POND SKATER

The Common Pond Skater lives on ponds and lakes across Europe. It has specially adapted feet which have a number of water-repelling hairs that provide enough area for it to move across the water without breaking through the surface film. It has very sensitive sense organs that can detect the vibrations of a drowning insect from some distance away. If other prey is not available, it will even eat the young of its own species. It is capable of sustained flight.

Descriptor: Linnaeus, 1758

Order: Hemiptera

Family: Gerridae

Genus: Gerris

Species: lacustris

Distribution: Across Europe

Size: ¾ in (20 mm)

WATER MEASURER *Hydrometra stagnorum*

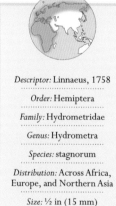

Descriptor: Linnaeus, 1758

Order: Hemiptera

Family: Hydrometridae

Genus: Hydrometra

Species: stagnorum

Distribution: Across Africa, Europe, and Northern Asia

Size: ½ in (15 mm)

A common species of water bug that is found across parts of Africa, Europe, and Asia, the Water Measurer lives at the edges of ponds, streams, and small rivers. These insects are predators and scavengers on small aquatic invertebrates, such as copepods and mosquito larvae as well as any creatures that fall into the water and drown. They have slender bodies, long legs, and specially adapted feet which allow them to stand on the surface film of fresh water.

Nepa cinerea WATER SCORPION

The Water Scorpion is found across Europe in ponds and streams where it is a voracious predator on a variety of aquatic creatures, ranging from mosquito larvae to tadpoles. The two front legs have evolved into a very effective seizure mechanism; the Water Scorpion waits for suitable prey to swim past, whereupon it snatches the victim and then drags it swiftly to the mouthparts. This insect breathes through its long tail, which at first glance looks like a stinger.

Descriptor: Linnaeus, 1758

Order: Hemiptera

Family: Nepidae

Genus: Nepa

Species: cinerea

Distribution: Across Europe

Size: Up to 1¼ in (30 mm)

WATER BOATMAN *Notonecta glauca*

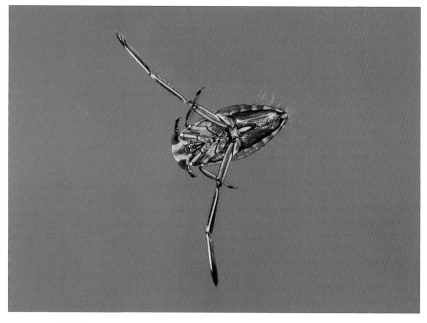

Descriptor: Linnaeus 1758

Order: Hemiptera

Family: Notonectidae

Genus: Notonecta

Species: glauca

Distribution: Across
Europe and Asia

Size: Up to ¾ in
(18 mm)

The Water Boatman is found in ponds and lakes across Europe and Asia, where it lives a curious upside-down life on the underside of the water's surface. For this reason, it is sometimes called a "backswimmer." It is a voracious predator that hunts small creatures, especially those that have accidentally fallen into the water. Any vibration that might indicate a potential meal will quickly attract any nearby water boatmen. If insufficient food is available, they will crawl out of the water and fly to another location.

Velia caprai WATER CRICKET

The Water Cricket lives on the surface film of water amongst rocks and vegetation at the edges of lakes, streams, and rivers across most of Europe and Asia. It is a predatory species that hunts tiny invertebrates. During the day these insects remain under cover, but at night they become very active, searching out potential prey, including things like mosquito eggs. The females lay their eggs in moss at the water's edge. These hatch as tiny nymphs, which quickly begin feeding on microscopic organisms in the water around them.

Descriptor: Tamanini, 1947

Order: Hemiptera

Family: Veliidae

Genus: Velia

Species: caprai

Distribution: Across Europe and into Asia

Size: Up to ¼ in (10 mm)

CICADAS

CLASS: INSECTA ORDER: HEMIPTERA; LINNAEUS, 1758
SUBORDER: AUCHENORRHYNCHA FAMILY: CICADIDAE
DISTRIBUTION: WARM TEMPERATE TO TROPICAL SIZE: ½–3 IN (12.5–75 MM)

Cicadas—of which there are about 2,500 different species of cicadas worldwide—are found in a variety of temperate and tropical regions. The larvae are almost never seen, however, as they live underground, feeding on the roots of various species of plants and trees. Although the adults are well known for producing loud songs, it is, in fact, only the males which make the noise known as "stridulation." After a pair has mated, the female typically cuts a slit into the bark of a tree or bush and lays her eggs there. When these hatch, the nymphs fall to the ground and then burrow into it, where they will remain until emerging several years later as adults.

Magicada spp PERIODICAL CICADAS

Periodical Cicadas all belong to the genus Magicada, and are so named because they appear in vast emergences on a strict annual schedule. Depending on the species, the adults emerge from their underground lives after either 13 or 17 years. Quite why they have settled on these numbers in their life-cycle is far from clear, but it is thought that this phasing evolved as part of an anti-predator or anti-parasite mechanism. Whatever the reasoning, it seems to be successful, because when they emerge, these harmless insects do so in unimaginable numbers—thought to be in the order of around 1.5 million cicadas per acre.

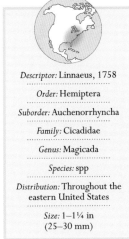

Descriptor: Linnaeus, 1758

Order: Hemiptera

Suborder: Auchenorrhyncha

Family: Cicadidae

Genus: Magicada

Species: spp

Distribution: Throughout the eastern United States

Size: 1–1¼ in (25–30 mm)

APHIDS

Class: Insecta Order: Hemiptera; Linnaeus, 1758
Suborder: Sternorrhyncha Superfamily: Aphidoidea
Distribution: Worldwide Size: ⅟25–⅜ in (1–9 mm)

Aphids are small sap-sucking insects that are often serious agricultural pests. There are around 4,000 species grouped into 10 families; these include the well-known greenfly and blackfly. These insects are capable of reproducing at an incredible rate—a single female can lead to over 40 generations in a single growing season. Fortunately, there are many insects which prey on them, including both the juvenile and adults of lacewings and ladybirds, as well as hoverfly larvae. Many aphids form close associations with ants in order to gain some protection. In return for this, they produce a sugar-rich liquid known as honeydew, which is irresistible to most ants. Adult aphids are able to fly, and are often carried significant distances by the wind.

Macrosiphum rosae ROSE APHID

Rose aphids, which are distributed worldwide, are well known to gardeners everywhere. They can become serious pests, as they not only suck the juices from their host plants—typically roses—but can also spread viral infections. They overwinter as eggs; these then hatch in Spring, and if left unchecked, can quickly reproduce to form extensive colonies. Rose aphids produce honeydew, a sugary substance much favored by ants. If enough of it builds up on the leaves, a black mold often develops on them. While ants will foster the aphids, other insects, such as ladybirds, hoverflies, lacewings, and parasitic wasps are their main predators.

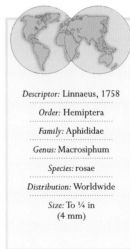

Descriptor: Linnaeus, 1758

Order: Hemiptera

Family: Aphididae

Genus: Macrosiphum

Species: rosae

Distribution: Worldwide

Size: To ¼ in
(4 mm)

MEALYBUGS

CLASS: INSECTA ORDER: HEMIPTERA; LINNAEUS, 1758
SUBORDER: STERNORRHYNCHA SUPERFAMILY: COCCOIDEA
FAMILY: PSEUDOCOCCIDAE
DISTRIBUTION: WORLDWIDE SIZE: $\frac{1}{25}$–$\frac{1}{4}$ IN (1–6 MM)

Mealybugs are a particular kind of scale insect. They lack an armored shield, but in its place they are covered with a white fibrous waxy layer. Their sap-sucking activities can make them a serious pest in both ornamental and commercial greenhouses, as well as on crops in the warmer climate areas. They produce large quantities of honeydew—this rich food source is often exploited by a black fungus. Once mature, the female mealybug lays between 200 and 600 eggs depending on the species, in a special structure called an ovisac. This is covered with waxy hairs to deter predators and parasites. The eggs hatch in about 10 days into young mealybugs called crawlers. A few species give birth to live young. Male mealybugs are short-lived, as they do not feed at all as adults and only live to fertilize the females.

SCALE INSECTS

CLASS: INSECTA ORDER: HEMIPTERA; LINNAEUS, 1758
SUBORDER: STERNORRHYNCHA SUPERFAMILY: COCCOIDEA
DISTRIBUTION: WORLDWIDE SIZE: ½₅–¼ IN (1–6 MM)

Scale insects are sap-sucking insects that are classified in the order of true bugs. There are about 8,000 species known to science, grouped into around 28 families. Physically, they have very low profiles, and have armored shields that are covered with a special waxy coating that displaces most liquids. This can make it hard to control their numbers with pesticides. They will attack a wide range of different plants, including many economically important crops. Some are less than ¼ in (2 mm) long, whereas others may be more than twice this size. As juveniles they are highly mobile, but once they reach the adult stage, the females of most species become immobile. The short-lived males, however, usually have one pair of wings, which are used for dispersal during the reproductive phase.

BEETLES

CLASS: INSECTA
ORDER: COLEOPTERA; LINNAEUS, 1758
DISTRIBUTION: WORLDWIDE   SIZE: ½25–6¼ IN (1–160 MM)

There are more species of beetles than any other insect on Earth, with about 350,000 having been described by science to date. It is thought that there may be ten to twenty times as many as this still undiscovered. They occupy almost every possible non-marine ecological niche, and vary from being economically beneficial (for example, ladybugs) to being serious pests of agriculture, commerce, and construction (these include grain weevils, woodworm, and such like). The environment is reliant on beetles to break down much of the dead animal and plant matter that continually accumulates. Beetles are holometabolous, with a full egg—larva—pupa —adult lifecycle. The adults generally have hard exoskeletons and tough wing cases called "elytra." Most beetles are able to fly, although some are flightless. Some have bright warning colors, whereas others use cryptic coloration to hide from predators. It is not uncommon for the males to have elaborate structures on their heads that are analogous to antlers—for example the Rhinoceros and Stag beetles.

SOLDIER BEETLE *Cantharis rustica*

Descriptor: Linnaeus, 1758

Order: Coleoptera

Family: Cantharidae

Genus: Cantharis

Species: rustica

Distribution: Across most of Europe

Size: ¾ in (18 mm)

Of the many species of Soldier Beetle, this one, *Cantharis rustica*, has no common name. It is common in gardens and on wild ground across most of Europe throughout the summer. The larvae are thin-bodied predators that feed on small invertebrates. While the adults are often seen on flowers, they are also predacious, and are, in fact, simply waiting for suitable prey. Aphids form a major part of their diet, but they also take flies, beetles, and other insects.

Rhagonycha fulva BLACK-TIPPED SOLDIER BEETLE

The Black-tipped Soldier Beetle is a common, often locally abundant, species that is widely distributed across Europe. It may be seen in gardens and wild habitats throughout the summer, and is especially fond of visiting the flowers of the Umbellifer family, including cow parsley, wild carrot, and others. There it feeds on nectar and pollen, but will, if the opportunity arises, also catch and eat other insects. The larvae are predators on small invertebrates such as slugs and snails.

Descriptor: Scopoli, 1763

Order: Coleoptera

Family: Cantharidae

Genus: Rhagonycha

Species: fulva

Distribution: Across Europe

Size: ¾ in
(20 mm)

GOLDEN GROUND BEETLE *Carabus auratus*

Descriptor: Linnaeus, 1761

Order: Coleoptera

Family: Carabidae

Genus: Carabus

Species: auratus

Distribution: Western and central Europe, introduced to the US

Size: ¾–1 in (17–22 mm)

The Golden Ground Beetle is found in western and central Europe, but is absent from the United Kingdom. It is now also found in the United States, having been introduced in the 1950s as a predator on the Gypsy Moth, a serious pest of American orchards. The larvae, which hunt in the early morning, are predacious on various small invertebrates. When they are fully grown, they burrow into the soil and pupate. They then emerge in the fall as spectacularly colored adults. They are relatively long-lived, surviving up to two years, during which time they are voracious predators on many insect pests, such as snails and slugs.

Chrysolina hyperici KLAMATH WEED BEETLE

A small metallic green insect that is sometimes used to help control the klamath weed (also known as St John's Wort), which can be a major agricultural nuisance. It was introduced to the Pacific coast region of the United States for this purpose. The eggs are laid on the undersides of klamath weed leaves, and the night-feeding larvae feed for about a month before pupating underground. This stage lasts just about under two weeks, whereupon the adults emerge. These also feed on leaves and flowers, concentrating on the upright new growth in the spring and moving to the low-growing foliage in wet weather.

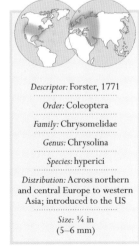

Descriptor: Forster, 1771

Order: Coleoptera

Family: Chrysomelidae

Genus: Chrysolina

Species: hyperici

Distribution: Across northern and central Europe to western Asia; introduced to the US

Size: ¼ in (5–6 mm)

POPLAR LEAF BEETLE

Chrysomela populi

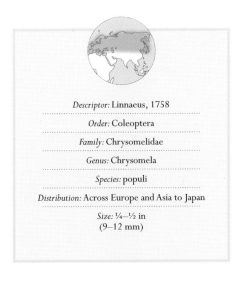

Also known as the Willow Leaf Beetle, the Poplar Leaf Beetle is a common species with bright red or orange wing cases that can be found in poplar and willow habitats across most of Europe and Asia. The sometimes locally abundant adults overwinter under bark, trash, or debris under or near trees. They begin to emerge in late March or early April and egg laying is underway by mid-April. They can then be seen through to the late summer months. Both the larvae and adults of this species feed on the leaves of willow, poplar, and aspen. When they are disturbed or threatened, they release a foul-smelling liquid.

Descriptor: Linnaeus, 1758

Order: Coleoptera

Family: Chrysomelidae

Genus: Chrysomela

Species: populi

Distribution: Across Europe and Asia to Japan

Size: ¼–½ in
(9–12 mm)

GREEN DOCK LEAF BEETLE *Gastrophysa viridula*

Descriptor: De Geer, 1775

Order: Coleoptera

Family: Chrysomelidae

Genus: Gastrophysa

Species: viridula

Distribution: Across Europe and Asia to Siberia and Korea; the United States

Size: ¼ in (4–6 mm)

The Green Dock Leaf Beetle can be seen across Europe, Asia, and the United States throughout the summer. As the name suggests, it feeds on the leaves of dock plants—the life-cycle begins with the yellow eggs being laid on the undersides of the leaves. After about a week, the black larvae hatch and begin feeding. There are three stages, after which they pupate and emerge as adults. These usually live about two to three weeks, but last much longer than this when overwintering.

Otiorhynchus sulcatus BLACK VINE WEEVIL

The Black Vine Weevil is a major pest on a wide variety of cultivated plants, especially those grown in containers. They are distributed worldwide, and the fact that the females are parthenogenetic—that is, they can lay fertile several hundred eggs without mating—makes them very difficult to control. The larvae feed voraciously on roots, which can quickly kill the plant concerned. The adults are nocturnal, hiding during the day and then crawling onto the foliage after dark.

Descriptor: Fabricius, 1775

Order: Coleoptera

Family: Curculionidae

Genus: Otiorhynchus

Species: sulcatus

Distribution: Worldwide

Size: ¼–½ in
(8–11 mm)

GREEN LEAF WEEVIL *Phyllobius pomaceus*

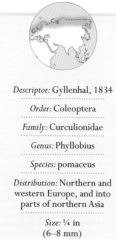

Descriptor: Gyllenhal, 1834

Order: Coleoptera

Family: Curculionidae

Genus: Phyllobius

Species: pomaceus

Distribution: Northern and western Europe, and into parts of northern Asia

Size: ¼ in (6–8 mm)

Also known as the "Nettle Weevil" or the "Green Nettle Weevil," the Green Leaf Weevil is a common species that is widely distributed across northern and western Europe. It has a black body that is around ¼ in (6–8 mm) long, covered with green scales, and its head features the characteristic weevil family snout. This species can often be seen on nettle leaves, on which both the larvae and adults feed. Although these weevils also eat the leaves of many garden plants, they seldom cause severe damage and can be easily controlled.

Oedemera nobilis THICK-LEGGED FLOWER BEETLE

The Thick-Legged Flower Beetle is a slender metallic green beetle that is found across southern Europe, where it can often be seen on flowers in gardens as well as on hedgerows and in other wild places. In the larval stages it lives and feeds inside the hollow stems of various plants. It then emerges as an adult in the early summer, when it feeds on pollen from flowers such as daisies, dandelions, and such like. The males have much thicker hind legs than the females, and it is these that are responsible for its common name.

Descriptor: Scopoli, 1763

Order: Coleoptera

Family: Oedemeridae

Genus: Oedemera

Species: nobilis

Distribution: Across southern Europe

Size: ¼ in (8–10 mm)

COMMON COCK-CHAFER OR MAY BUG
Melolontha melolontha

The Common Cockchafer or May Bug is a common European beetle that is frequently attracted to light in the early summer, when it often causes some consternation. It is, however, completely harmless, in spite of its large size and loud, buzzing flight. The larvae are white grubs that feed underground on the roots of various grasses for up to five years. They then pupate at the end of fall, over-wintering in this state before emerging the following May or June. Adult cockchafers eat the leaves and flowers of many deciduous trees, shrubs, and other plants, but rarely cause any serious damage.

Descriptor:	Linnaeus, 1758
Order:	Coleoptera
Family:	Scarabaeidae
Genus:	Melolontha
Species:	melolontha
Distribution:	Across Europe

Size: 1½–2 in
(40–50 mm)

WASP BEETLE *Clytus arietis*

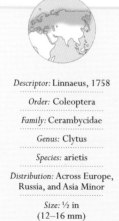

Descriptor: Linnaeus, 1758

Order: Coleoptera

Family: Cerambycidae

Genus: Clytus

Species: arietis

Distribution: Across Europe, Russia, and Asia Minor

Size: ½ in
(12–16 mm)

This is a common species of beetle that is distributed across Europe, Russia, and Asia Minor, where it may be seen in early summer on flowers in backyards and wild places. It has distinctive wasp-like markings that provide it with an effective means of protection from predators. In spite of the warning colors, it is, in fact, completely harmless. The legs are orange-brown, the two hind pairs rather longer than the front. The antennae are brown with black tips. The larvae feed on dead wood for up to two years, whereas the adults feed on flower pollen.

Rhagium bifasciatum TWO-BANDED
LONGHORN BEETLE

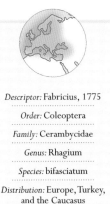

The Two-banded Longhorn Beetle is found across southern and central Europe, Turkey, and the Caucasus. The life-cycle begins when eggs are laid in dead wood—often that of conifers. The larvae then hatch and feed on the wood, boring holes through it for about two years. They then pupate before emerging as adults. These feed on the leaves of various deciduous and coniferous trees. This beetle may reach 1in (24 mm) long and can be distinguished by the two prominent pale yellow bands on each side of its back, although up to seventeen different patterns have been recognized in this species.

Descriptor: Fabricius, 1775

Order: Coleoptera

Family: Cerambycidae

Genus: Rhagium

Species: bifasciatum

Distribution: Europe, Turkey, and the Caucasus

Size: ¾–1 in
(20–24 mm)

LADYBUGS

CLASS: INSECTA ORDER: COLEOPTERA; LINNAEUS, 1758
SUPERFAMILY: CUCUJOIDEA FAMILY: COCCINELLIDAE
DISTRIBUTION: WORLDWIDE SIZE: ⅛–⅜ IN (3–9 MM)

Ladybugs (also called "lady birds" in some parts of the world) are small often brightly-colored beetles in the family Coccinellidae. About 5,000 species have been described so far, and doubtless more remain to be discovered. They are nearly all predators on a variety of insects in both the larval and adult form. Since most of the prey species are classed as pests of agriculture or backyards, they are consequently almost universally welcomed wherever they occur. The exceptions to this include some of the herbivorous species such as the Mexican bean beetle, which can be very destructive. Ladybugs vary in size from around ¼ in (1 mm) up to about ½ in (10 mm), and while a large number have red, yellow, or orange coloration, others are dark brown or even black.

2-SPOT LADYBUG *Adalia bipunctata*

Descriptor: Linnaeus, 1758

Order: Coleoptera

Family: Coccinellidae

Genus: Adalia

Species: bipunctata

Distribution: Across Europe, Central Asia, and North America

Size: Body length: ¼ in (4–5 mm)

Also known as the "Lady Bird" or "Lady Beetle," the adult 2-Spot Ladybug is typically red with prominent two black spots; however, the species is highly variable and other forms may be seen. It is widely distributed across Europe, Central Asia, and North America, where it is welcomed by gardeners due to its voracious appetite for aphids, in both the larval and adult forms. The eggs are laid in small batches—these then hatch into larvae that have thick-set bodies and, unlike the adults, no wings. After four stages, they pupate and a week or so later the adult emerges.

Coccinella septempunctata 7-SPOT LADYBUG

The 7-Spot Ladybug is well-known to gardeners across most of the northern hemisphere, being one of the most common species throughout its range. It can be easily identified by the presence of three black spots on each of the red wing cases, with a further spot that lies across them. This coloration is used to warn predators of the toxic chemicals it carries. The larvae are dark and alligator-like with three pairs of prominent legs. Like other ladybugs, it has an incredible appetite for aphids—as a consequence of this, it was introduced to North America many years ago.

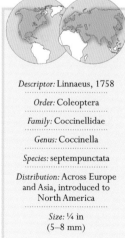

Descriptor: Linnaeus, 1758

Order: Coleoptera

Family: Coccinellidae

Genus: Coccinella

Species: septempunctata

Distribution: Across Europe and Asia, introduced to North America

Size: ¼ in
(5–8 mm)

14-SPOT LADYBUG

Propylea quatuordecimpunctata

A small yellow insect with fourteen black spots on its wing cases. It is found across most of Europe, and many years ago was accidentally introduced to North America. Since then, it has been deliberately reintroduced in many states in an attempt to control the Russian Wheat Aphid. However, recent research indicates that despite the release of more than half a million laboratory-reared specimens in 16 western states of the US, there are still no completely established populations in the west. As with the other ladybug species, it is a voracious hunter of aphids in both the larval and adult forms. These are separated by a pupal stage that lasts about two weeks.

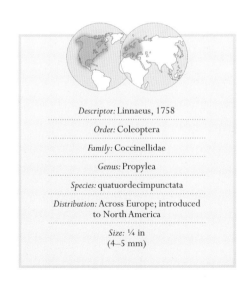

Descriptor: Linnaeus, 1758

Order: Coleoptera

Family: Coccinellidae

Genus: Propylea

Species: quatuordecimpunctata

Distribution: Across Europe; introduced to North America

Size: ¼ in
(4–5 mm)

NEUROPTERANS

CLASS: INSECTA SUPERORDER: ENDOPTERYGOTA
ORDER: NEUROPTERA; LINNAEUS, 1758
DISTRIBUTION: WORLDWIDE SIZE: ⅜–3 IN (9–75 MM)

The order Neuroptera contains around 5,000 species of different insect types, including Alderflies, Antlions, Dobsonflies, Lacewings, Mantidflies, Owlflies, Snakeflies, and Spongeflies. These are generally characterized by the adults having excellent vision, soft bodies, four veined wings, and a slow fluttering flight. Their heavily veined wings are usually folded back over their bodies when they are at rest. Their larvae are predators, with some being significant components in the natural control of insect pests such as aphids, mites, leafhoppers, beetles, scale insects, and caterpillars. In order to camouflage themselves, the larvae of many species cover their bodies with detritus—mostly the empty skins of the insects they have eaten. The larval stages of some neuropterans such as alderflies and dobsonflies are aquatic. These seek out and attack small creatures, and then suck out their body fluids through hollow feeding tubes. As adults, some do not feed, but those that do either consume various fluids, dead animals, or the nectar from flowers.

LACEWINGS

CLASS: INSECTA ORDER: NEUROPTERA;
LINNAEUS, 1758
DISTRIBUTION: WORLDWIDE SIZE: ⅜–3 IN (9–75 MM)

Lacewings are members of the order *Neuroptera*, which contains some 4,000 species. They have four veined wings, and a slow fluttering flight. Their larvae are predators on many insect pests such as aphids as well as mites, leafhoppers, beetles, scale insects, and caterpillars. Lacewing larvae have unusual sucking mouthparts, with a pair of extremely long, slender, and conspicuous mandibles (or jaws) that curve forward from the front of the head. These mandibles are tubular structures, rather like a pair of hypodermic needles, which are sunk into the victim's body. The larva then sucks out the body fluids of its prey as if through two tiny drinking straws. In order to camouflage themselves, the larvae cover their bodies with detritus—mostly the empty skins of the insects they have eaten. As adults, they eat nectar from flowers, and so act as pollinators. Following mating, the females lay around 300 eggs, each of which is at the end of a long, thin stalk. It has been estimated that each larva that survives to adulthood eats somewhere between 1,000 and 10,000 aphids in its lifetime.

Osmylus fulvicephalus GIANT OR STREAM LACEWING

The Giant or Stream Lacewing is a large lacewing that can be found in late spring and early summer in damp areas near rivers and streams. It is distributed across much of central Europe; however, being mostly crepuscular in its behavior, it is not often seen during the day. The Giant Lacewing's eggs are laid in vegetation along the edges of running water, and when the larvae hatch, they are predators on a wide variety of small invertebrates.

Descriptor: Scopoli, 1763

Order: Neuroptera

Family: Osmylidae

Genus: Osmylus

Species: fulvicephalus

Distribution: Across central Europe

Size: Wingspan: 2 in (50 mm)

ANTLIONS

CLASS: INSECTA ORDER: NEUROPTERA; LINNAEUS, 1758
SUPERFAMILY: MYRMELEONTOIDEA FAMILY: MYRMELEONTIDAE
DISTRIBUTION: WARM TEMPERATE TO TROPICAL SIZE: ½–3 IN (12.5–75 MM)

Antlions are neuropteran insects that as larvae are fierce predators on small invertebrates, and are especially good at capturing ants. They can be found in most parts of the world, with sandy places being favored. This is because many species build cone-shaped pitfall traps in soft, dry soils. The larva, which has huge pincer-like jaws, hides in a small tunnel at the bottom of the cone, and waits for an ant to walk by. The sides of the cone are deliberately built to be unstable, and so the ant is doomed to fall into the grasp of the antlion below. The larvae of some species do not build pits but roam freely looking for prey. As adults, they have four veined wings, and fly in the evenings in search of a mate, in the manner of a weak damselfly. Although they greatly resemble damselflies, antlions belong to an entirely different order of insects. The adult antlion can be readily distinguished from a damselfly by its long, clubbed antennae. Unlike their larvae, adult antlions feed on pollen and nectar. They are sometimes called the "nerve-winged insects" due to the elaborate pattern of longitudinal and cross-veins (nerves) that spreads across their four wings.

Palpares libelluloides ANT LION

The Ant Lion is a large neuropteran member of the *Myrmeleontidae* family which is found across the more arid regions of southern Europe. The larvae are voracious predators on many small invertebrates, especially ants. They have large curved mandibles: when they have captured their prey, they suck its juices out through the hollow jaws. The adults of this species can have wingspans of up to 5 in (125 mm), and look very similar to dragonflies. They are, however, very weak fliers and generally keep low to the ground.

Descriptor: Linnaeus, 1764

Order: Neuroptera

Family: Myrmeleonidae

Genus: Palpares

Species: libelluloides

Distribution: Southern Europe

Size: Males: 4–4½ in (105–115 mm) Females: 4¾–5 in (120–125 mm)

COMMON ALDER FLY *Sialis lutaria*

Descriptor: Linnaeus, 1758

Order: Neuroptera

Family: Megaloptera

Genus: Sialis

Species: lutaria

Distribution: Across Europe and Russia

Size: ½–1 in (16–22 mm)

The Common Alder Fly is found near streams and slow-moving rivers across much of Europe, as well as into parts of Russia. Despite its name, it has no association with alder trees, other than being found on foliage beside river banks, which is where alder is usually found. The eggs are laid on vegetation along the edges of flowing water, and when the larvae hatch they are predators of many small aquatic creatures. It can take several years for them to become fully grown—at this point, they crawl out of the water and pupate in soft soil or under suitable cover such as large stones. The adults, which have two pairs of wings, emerge a short time later but do not live very long—a few days at most.

Libelloides coccajus EUROPEAN OWLFLY

F ound in mountainous areas in south-eastern
Europe, the European Owlfly resembles a cross
between an antlion, a butterfly, and a dragonfly. They
have long antennae with large knobs on the end, and a
bright yellow coloration on their wings. They are active
during the day, and capable of fast flight, which they
use to good effect catching various kinds of insects
whilst on the wing. After mating, the females lay their
eggs under small stones or pieces of wood. After the
larvae have hatched, they lie in wait for small creatures
to walk past, and then pounce and consume them.
When they are fully grown, they pupate in a silken
cocoon, emerging later as adults.

Descriptor: Denis &
Schiffermüller, 1775

Order: Neuroptera

Family: Ascalaphidae

Genus: Libelloides

Species: coccajus

Distribution: South-eastern
Europe

Size: 1¾–2 in
(45–50 mm)

OTHER INSECT ORDERS

Although the main insect orders have been covered thus far, there are several others which have not. This is because some have been extinct for many millions of years, whereas others live extremely reclusive lives in remote places and are unlikely to be encountered except by intrepid scientists. A good example of this is the Order Mantophasmatodea, which consists of insects known as "gladiators" that are only found in small areas in Namibia. Likewise, the Order Grylloblattodea is made up of wingless insects which are only found at the tops of certain mountains in extremely cold environments. This has led to them being known variously as "rock crawlers" or "icebugs." A few other orders have not been covered because the insects they contain are so small that they require specialist equipment in order to be identified. Most of the remaining orders are presented in this section, and include some truly fascinating creatures. The Praying Mantis, for instance, could be mistaken for an alien visitor, and the cockroach (pictured here), whilst being a major pest species, is one of nature's great success stories, being one of the hardiest animals on the planet.

EUROPEAN EARWIG *Forficula auricularia*

Descriptor: Linnaeus, 1758

Order: Dermaptera

Family: Forficulidae

Genus: Forficula

Species: auricularia

Distribution: Throughout the northern hemisphere

Size: ½ in (12–15 mm)

Earwigs are insects that belong to the order *Dermaptera*—there are about 1,800 species distributed across ten families. They are found worldwide, and none are thought to be harmful in any way, despite their fearsome tail pincers (*cerci*). The commonest species in the northern hemisphere is the European Earwig, having been artificially spread by human activity. It first reached the United States in the 1900s—since then, it has established itself throughout many parts of the country. The females lay their eggs in the fall, and then overwinter. In the spring, they guard over them and then tend the young once they have hatched. Their diet is very varied, including leaves, fruit, decomposing plant matter, and other insects.

Incisitermes minor WESTERN DRYWOOD TERMITE

The Western Drywood Termite is a common social insect that has become a serious economic pest. It occurs naturally in California where it infests dead wood. Unfortunately, human structures made of timber are so close to its natural habitat that it will quickly exploit them, given the opportunity. Besides occurring in the western states, this species has also established itself in numerous small pockets along parts of the east coast of the United States from Florida up to Virginia. There are four forms of this termite—the queen, the workers, the soldiers, and the swarmers or "alates" (these are winged males and females). If successful in mating, some alates will become royal pairs—that is to say, the kings and queens of new colonies of termites.

Descriptor: Hagen, 1858

Order: Isoptera

Family: Kalotermitidae

Genus: Incisitermes

Species: minor

Distribution: The United States and Mexico

Size: Swarmer: ½ in (11–12 mm)
Soldier: ¼–½ in (8–12 mm)
Worker: ½ in (11–12 mm)

HOG LOUSE *Haematopinus suis*

Descriptor: Linnaeus, 1758

Order: Mallophaga

Family: Haematopinidae

Genus: Haematopinus

Species: suis

Distribution: Worldwide

Size: ¼ in
(5–6 mm)

A wingless blood-sucking ectoparasite that lives on the skin of pigs, where it is usually found hidden in amongst folds of flesh, the Hog Louse is distributed worldwide, and can carry a wide variety of infectious diseases. The persistent loss of blood and intense itching that the bites cause can result in stunted growth and other husbandry problems. These lice live for about a month, during which time they can grow to ¼ in (6 mm) long. The females lay several eggs a day, each of which is glued to the host's bristles—these then take between two and three weeks to hatch.

Empusa pennata EMPUSID MANTIS

The Empusid Mantis inhabits south-western Europe, where it can be found in a wide variety of wild habitats; it is smaller than the European Praying Mantis. Empusid Mantids survive the winter months as young nymphs and therefore adults and young of these long-lived insects may be observed together during the late summer months. Once the female nymphs have reached maturity at the age of about one month, they begin releasing a scent attractant at night to call males. Unlike many other mantid species, Empusid Mantis females do not kill the males whilst mating.

Descriptor: Thunberg, 1815

Order: Mantodea

Family: Empusidae

Genus: Empusa

Species: pennata

Distribution: South-western Europe

Size: 2–2½ in (45–70 mm)

EUROPEAN PRAYING MANTIS *Mantis religiosa*

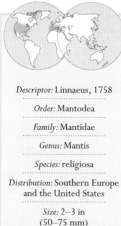

Descriptor: Linnaeus, 1758

Order: Mantodea

Family: Mantidae

Genus: Mantis

Species: religiosa

Distribution: Southern Europe and the United States

Size: 2–3 in (50–75 mm)

A common species that was originally only found in southern Europe, following an accidental introduction in 1899 the European Praying Mantis is now also distributed across a large part of the United States. It is a voracious predator on insects and other small creatures. It operates by hiding in foliage and pouncing on any prey that passes within range using its powerful front legs. It is helped in this by having excellent camouflage provided by its green coloration. The life-cycle of the European Praying Mantis begins when the eggs are laid in an egg mass called an ootheca. The mantids nymphs are also predacious.

Panorpa communis COMMON SCORPIONFLY

The Common Scorpionfly is found on rough ground and along hedgerows across many parts of southern and central Europe. Scorpionflies belong to an ancient group of insects known as "mecopterans" which can be traced back more than 250 million years. They feed mostly on dead insects and fruit, with a large proportion of their diet being made up of creatures stolen from spiders' webs. The common name of the species comes from the fact that the males have long tails with a scorpion-like "stinger" on the end. This is, in fact, an entirely harmless structure used to hold the female during mating.

Descriptor: Linnaeus, 1758

Order: Mecoptera

Family: Panorpidae

Genus: Panorpa

Species: communis

Distribution: Across many parts of southern and central Europe

Size: ¾–1 in
(22–24 mm)

STICK INSECTS

CLASS: INSECTA

ORDER: PHASMATODEA; JACOBSON & BIANCHI, 1902

DISTRIBUTION: SUB-TROPICAL AND TROPICAL SIZE: ½–13 IN (12.5–330 MM)

The Order *Phasmatodea* is comprised of plant-eating insects known variously as stick insects, walking sticks, or leaf insects. These curious creatures are superbly adapted from a camouflage perspective—in their natural environments they can be exceptionally difficult to see. So far, in the order of 2,800 species have been described for science; however, it is likely that many more remain to be discovered. Stick insects are mostly tropical, although a few species can be found in sub-tropical and the warmer temperate regions. The largest ones can reach to around 12 in (330 mm) in length, and others can weigh over 1.76 oz (50g). Many stick insects reproduce by parthenogenesis, and therefore do not need males to become fertile. They are capable of producing large numbers of eggs when the conditions are right. After a few weeks, these hatch into miniature replicas of the adults, whereupon they begin feeding almost immediately. They pass through a number of stages before reaching maturity.

LEAF INSECTS

CLASS: INSECTA ORDER: PHASMATODEA; JACOBSON & BIANCHI, 1902
SUPERFAMILY: PHYLLIOIDEA FAMILY: PHYLLIIDAE
DISTRIBUTION: TROPICAL SIZE: ½–3 IN (12.5–75 MM)

Leaf insects—also known as "walking leaves"—are closely related to stick insects and are found in tropical regions from South Asia down to Australia. The earliest *Phasmids* probably arose around 225 million years ago; however, the leaf insects seem to have first evolved around fifty million years ago. They do not appear to have changed significantly since then; these days the *Phylliidae* family is comprised of 36 known species, are all of which are leaf mimics. The leaf insects are entirely herbivorous, as their name suggests, feeding on the leaves of various plants and shrubs at night, and lying at rest during the day. Many have developed a truly remarkable camouflage in order to avoid being detected by predators. Once they have reached maturity, female leaf insects usually lay a few eggs every day.

SILVERFISH
Lepisma saccharina

The Silverfish is a primitive flightless insect that can be found in dark places in houses across the world. The group of insects that it belongs to—*Thysanura*—are often referred to as "bristletails," due to the numerous, fairly lengthy filaments which project from their tails. It is thought that the silverfish has changed little since it first evolved around 300 million years ago. Its common name derives from the creature's silvery-blue color, combined with the fish-like appearance of its movements, while the scientific name indicates the silverfish's diet of carbohydrates, such as sugar or starches. They are minor pests of households, in that they will eat a variety of items such as paper, cotton, linen, wallpaper, glue and such like.

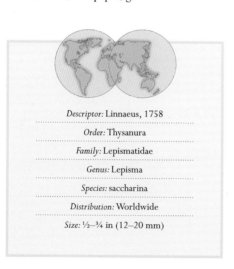

Descriptor: Linnaeus, 1758

Order: Thysanura

Family: Lepismatidae

Genus: Lepisma

Species: saccharina

Distribution: Worldwide

Size: ½–¾ in (12–20 mm)

GLOSSARY

Abdomen The division of an insect's body that carries the digestive and reproductive organs.

Antennae The pair of sensory organs on an insect's head that are sometimes referred to as "feelers."

Aquatic A creature that lives in water.

Brood A generation of young.

Carnivorous A plant or animal that feeds on the flesh of animals.

Caterpillar The larval stage of a butterfly or moth.

Chitin The tough material from which an insect's cuticle is made.

Chrysalis The pupa of a butterfly.

Cocoon The case that is made by many insect larvae to protect the pupa.

Compound Eye A multi-faceted eye that is only found in arthropods such as insects.

Cremaster The hook-like structure from which a butterfly or moth pupa hangs.

Drone A male honey bee.

Ecdysis The process whereby an insect sheds its skin between molts.

Elytra The wing cases of a beetle or earwig.

Exoskeleton The hard outer skeleton of an animal such as an insect or crustacean.

Frenulum A special structure that stops the hind wings of a butterfly or moth from getting tangled with the fore wings.

Grub A particular type of insect larva typified by certain beetle larvae.

Hemimetabolous An insect that has a life history which features incomplete metamorphosis.

Imago The adult stage of an insect.

Insect An animal which in the adult stage has a body that is divided into three parts—a head, thorax, and abdomen. The thorax has three segments, each with a pair of legs.

Instar The stage between two molts in an insect's life history.

Larva The stage in an insect's life history that comes after the egg—often referred to as a caterpillar, maggot, or grub.

Mandible An animal's jaw.

Metamorphosis The process whereby an insect changes from one stage to another, such as from pupa to adult.

Molt The process whereby an animal sheds its skin.

Nocturnal An organism that is active at night.

Ootheca The egg case produced by insects such as cockroaches and praying mantids.

Oviparous An animal that lays its eggs outside its body.

Ovipositor A long, thin egg-laying tube.

Pheromone A scent that is used as a mate attractant by many animals.

Predator An animal that feeds by killing and eating other animals.

Pupate The process by which a larva metamorphoses into a pupa.

Social Animals that live in organized groups.

Spiracle Respiratory openings typically located along the sides of an insect's body.

Tympanum A hearing membrane found in certain insects and many higher animals.

Veins The strengthening ribs found in an insect's wing.

Viviparous The term used for giving birth to live young.

INDEX

Acherontia atropos 92
Acronicta psi 85
Adalia bipunctata 224
Aeshna cyanea 105
Aglais urticae 56
alder flies 234
anatomy scheme 14
Angle Shades 86
ant lions 232–3
Anthocharis cardamines 68
ants 164–7
Aphantopus hyperantus 74
aphids 200–1
Argynnis aglaja 58
Argynnis paphia 60
Aricia agestis 48
Azure Damselfly 120

Banded Demoiselle 117
Bath White 73
Beautiful Demoiselle 118
bees 148–52
bees, wasps, sawflies, and
    ants 146–67
beetles 206–27
behavior and sociality 36
Biston betularia 84
Black & Red Froghopper
    185
Black Ant 167
Black Scavenger Fly 134
Black Swallowtail 66

Black Vine Weevil 215
Black-tipped Soldier
    Beetle 209
Blow-Flies 144
Blue-Winged Grasshopper
    172
Brimstone 70
Broad-Bodied Chaser 108
Brown Argus 48
Brown Hairstreak 54
bumblebees 152
bush crickets 174
butterflies 42–79

caddisflies 128
Callophrys rubi 49
Calopteryx splendens 117
Calopteryx virgo 118
Cantharis rustica 208
Carabus auratus 210
Celastrina argiolus 50
Celithemis eponina 106
Cercopis vulnerata 185
Chorthippus parallelus 171
Chrysolina hyperici 211
Chrysomela populi 213
cicadas 198–9
Cinnabar Moth 83
Clouded Yellow 69
Clytus arietis 220
Coccinella septempunctata 225
Coenagrion puella 120

Coenonympha pamphilus 75
Coleoptera 206–27
Colias croceus 69
Comma 64
Common Alder Fly 234
Common Blue 52
Common Blue Damselfly
    122
Common Cockchafer 218
Common Darter 114
Common Green
    Grasshopper 173
Common Pond Skater
    193
Common Scorpionfly
    243
communication 31
conservation 39
Coreus marginatus 188
crickets 174–80

Damselflies 116–28
Danaus plexippus 44
Dark Bush Cricket 176
Dark Green Fritillary 58
Death's-Head Hawkmoth
    92
Deilephila elpenor 93
Deilephila porcellus 94
Dermaptera 238
Diptera 130–45
Dock Leaf Bug 188

dragonflies 104–15
dragonflies and damselflies
    102–29

earwigs 238
Eight-Spotted Skimmer
    110
Elephant Hawkmoth 93
Emperor Moth 90
Empusa pennata 241
Empusid Mantis 241
Enallagma cyathigerum 122
Epaulet Skimmer 113
Ephemeroptera 124
Euphydryas aurinia 61
European Cicada 198
European Crane Fly 135
European Earwig 238
European Owlfly 235
European Praying Mantis
    242
evolution 30

flies 130–45
Forficula auricularia 238
Formica rufa 166
froghoppers 184–5

Gastrophysa viridula 214
Gatekeeper 79
Gerris lacustris 193
Giant Ichneumon Wasp 157

Golden Ground beetle
    210
Gonepteryx rhamni 70
Graphosoma lineatum 190
grasshoppers 170–3
Gray Dagger 85
Grayling 76
Great Green Bush-Cricket
    177
Green Dock Leaf Beetle
    214
Green Hairstreak 49
Green Leaf Weevil 216
Green Sawfly 161
Green Shield Bug 191
Green Silver-Lines 87

habitats 37
Haematopinus suis 240
Halloween Pennant 106
Hemiptera 182–205
Hipparchia semele 76
Hog Louse 240
Holly Blue 50
honey bees 150
hornets 162–3
horse flies 140
hoverflies 138
human-insect interaction
    38
Hummingbird Hawkmoth
    96

Hydrometra stagnorum 194
Hymenoptera 146–67

Inachis io 62
Incisitermes minor 239
insect orders, other
    236–49
insect, the life of an 21
Insecta 43
Iron Prominent 88
Isoptera 239

Klamath Weed Beetle 211

lacewings 230
Ladybug, 14-Spot 226
Ladybug, 2-Spot 224
Ladybug, 7-Spot 225
ladybugs 222–6
Large Red Damselfly 123
Large Skipper 46
Large White 71
Lasius niger 167
leaf insects 246
Lepidoptera 42–101
Lepisma saccharina 248
Leptophyes punctatissima
    175
Libelloides coccajus 235
Libellula depressa 108
Libellula forensis 110
Libellula luctuosa 111

Libellula pulchella 112
life-cycles 22–29
Lime Hawkmoth 98
Lobster Moth 89
locomotion 34
Lycaena phlaeas 51

Macroglossum stellatarum 96
Macrosiphum rosae 201
Magicada spp 199
Mallophaga 240
Maniola jurtina 77
Mantis religiosa 242
Mantodea 241
Marsh Fritillary 61
mayflies 124
Meadow Brown 77
Meadow Grasshopper 171
mealybugs 202
Mecoptera 243
Melolontha melolontha 219
Millet Skipper 47
Mimas tiliae 98
mole crickets 178
Monarch 44
mosquitoes 142
moths 80–101

naming and taxonomy 41
Nepa cinerea 195
nervous system 15
Neuroptera 228–35
Neuropterans 228–35

Notodonta dromedarius 88
Notonecta glauca 196

Ochlodes venata 46
Odonata 102–23
Oedemera nobilis 217
Oedipoda caerulescens 172
Omocestus viridulus 173
Orange Tip 68
Oriental Hornet 163
Orthetrum chrysostigma 113
Orthoptera 168–81
Osmylus fulvicephalus 231
Otiorhynchus sulcatus 215
owl flies 235

Painted Lady 65
Palomena prasina 191
Palpares libelluloides 233
Panorpa communis 243
Papilio polyxenes 66
Pararge aegeria 78
Peacock 62
Pelopidas thrax 47
Peppered Moth 84
Periodical Cicada 199
Phasmatodea 244–7
Phlogophora meticulosa 86
Pholidoptera griseoaptera 176
Phyllobius pomaceus 216
Pieris brassicae 71
Pieris rapae 72
Plecoptera 126
Polistes olivaceus 156

Polygonia c-album 64
Polyommatus icarus 52
Pond Skater 193
Pontia daplidice 73
Poplar Leaf Beetle 212
predators 39
Privet Hawkmoth 99
Propylea quatuordecimpunctata 226
Pseudoips prasinana 87
Pyronia tithonus 79
Pyrrhosoma nymphula 123

Red-Black Shield Bug 190
Red-Brown Paper Wasp 156
Rhagium bifasciatum 221
Rhagonycha fulva 209
Rhogogaster viridis 161
Rhyssa persuasoria 157
Ringlet 74
Robber Flies 136
Rose Aphid 201

Saturnia (Pavonia) pavonia 90
sawflies 160–61
scale insects 204
Scathophaga stercoraria 132
Sepsis fulgens 134
shield bugs 186–91
Sialis lutaria 234
Silverfish 248

Silver-Washed Fritillary 60
Six-Spot Burnet 100
sizes 18
Small Copper 51
Small Elephant Hawkmoth
    94
Small Heath 75
Small Tortoiseshell 56
Small White 72
Soldier Beetle 208
Southern Hawker 105
Southern Wood Ant 166
Speckled Bush-Cricket
    175
Speckled Wood 78
Sphecid Wasps 158
Sphinx ligustri 99
Spilosoma lubricipeda 82
Stauropus fagi 89
stick insects 244
stoneflies 126

stream lacewing 231
structure and form 12
Sympetrum striolatum 114

Tettigonia viridissima 177
Thecla betulae 54
Thick-Legged Flower
    Beetle 217
Thysanura 248
Tipula paludosa 135
Trichoptera 128
Trithemis annulata 115
true bugs 182–205
true crickets 180
Twelve-Spotted Skimmer
    112
Two-Banded Longhorn
    Beetle 221
Tyria jacobaeae 83

Vanessa cardui 65

Velia caprai 197
Vespa orientalis 163
Violet Darter/Violet
    Dropwing 115

Wasp Beetle 220
wasps 154–8
Water Boatman 196
water bugs 192–99
Water Cricket 197
Water Measurer 194
Water Scorpion 195
Western Drywood
    Termite 239
White Ermine 82
Widow Skimmer 111

Yellow Dung Fly 132

Zygaena filipendulae 100

PICTURE CREDITS

The majority of the photographs that appear in this book were taken by the author, Patrick Hook. The author and publishers would like to thank the following individuals and organizations for their contributions.